THE SPANISH SCENE

FICTION BY CHANDLER BROSSARD

THE
SPANISH
SCENE

CHANDLER
BROSSARD

New York / THE VIKING PRESS

This book is for
DR. JAMES E. THOMPSON,
who saved my life

THE SPANISH SCENE

"Papa," the boy said, pointing to the two gray-uniformed Civil Guardsmen strolling in the Pyrenees Mountains. "Look! They have different guns. Why?"

His suntanned, open-shirted father said softly, "One is a machine gun for shooting people close by. The other one has a rifle to shoot people far away. Now stop asking questions. They might hear you."

In Madrid, we were walking on the wide, furious Paseo del Prado, Luis the writer and I, beneath the sleepy chestnut trees, and his flitting blue eyes and intensity made the day seem muscular. "I am like a tree," he said, flinging his hand into the air. "My branches go all over the place, but my roots are in Spain. In my mind, of course, I am all kinds of things and people, that is what a fiction writer is, a living repertory theater, but in my heart I am simply and completely a Spaniard. You speak of the alienation of the writer in your country. In Spain we do not know what that means. I am not alienated from my culture, I am my culture."

A tiny black Seat darted in front of us. "Cars!" he muttered after dodging it. "Everyone in Madrid has a car. Can you imagine? You know, American writers seem to dislike, even hate, their own society. They seem so very unhappy. This is very different from being tragic, of having the what Unamuno called tragic sense of life. The very things that define you in your humanness are your limitations. The Spaniard asks, Who am I? The American asks, Why am I me? It is true that we do not have political freedom. But is there really political freedom anywhere? I wonder. Our kind of nonfreedom is simply more obvious."

He lit a racy-smelling Spanish cigarette. We passed a blind woman who was selling national lottery tickets. "This is your lucky day!" she cried. "Your fortune awaits you!" Luis filled the air with lovely white smoke. "You ask about the Church in Spain. I am afraid that foreigners do not understand the function of the Church here. It has nothing to do with religion. That is a ritual people were performing long before the Church. No. Its function has been to unify the country. Spain has always been broken up into so many different little regions, little countries, with so many different habits and thoughts keeping them apart. The Church has been the only structure that all shared, in a way. It has taken the place of a stable government. The priests have been its constant ministers."

A cool-faced girl with a splendid, somnolent body was coming toward us. A young man walking ahead of us leaped into the endless Spanish game. "You fill me with poetry," he said to her. "You are the most dazzling star in the heavens. When I look at you my blood . . ." She kept right on walking, a slight smile at her mouth. In the distance a church bell tolled heavily.

"But do you know what is unifying Spain now?" Luis went on. "It is so funny. Television. It is bringing all the peoples together through showing them what is going on in the world, and in Spain too. For the first time. They can see France and America and Africa. And princesses and movie stars. Ay! Before they lived only in their little villages and their isolated fantasies.

Of course, it is ruining their night social life in the streets and bars."

I glanced at an ancient baroque door and asked him about censorship on television. He giggled happily. "Oh it is wonderful! It is the wildest, silliest little game! The censors take out what they think the people think the censors think they should be taking out. Ay! What effect does their nonsense have on the writers? I'll tell you. It helps them be better writers. Since you cannot come out and say, 'There is no God, there is no justice,' you must show it, and indirectly. And what better discipline can you ask for? You know another thing television is doing is showing the Mass sung in ordinary language. Now the people understand it for the first time in their lives. Ah, yes. It is very amusing, no?"

We turned into a cool cobblestoned side street, untouched by the dry Spanish street heat, and entered a bar for a coffee. The big, gentle room was vibrating with conversation and simple human pleasure. The delighted people here were not afraid to touch each other and laugh. An old man at our marble-top table was snoozing over a half-finished brandy. "You asked me before what it is like to be a Spanish writer," Luis said, sipping the small black coffee. "I will tell you. Spaniards have a special respect, perhaps awe, for the writer. They feel that he is a kind of magician. Possibly this is because of the formerly great amount of illiteracy among the masses. Because the written word was a mystery to them, they thought that anyone who could create something out of this mystery had to be more than human." He waved gaily at a dark man with a long, twisted nose.

"I may not have any money—writers in Spain must scuffle like forest creatures in order to survive, but isn't that the case everywhere?—but I have prestige. When an article of mine appears, all the neighbors make a point of telling my wife they have read it, and they are proud of this situation. And I get many letters. Now this is rare, oh yes. To get a letter of praise from a Spaniard is a true event. Unlike the American, he does not feel that writing public letters is one of life's necessities." He shook his head and smiled. "You know, the position of the intellectual here is very difficult. You must think either against or for the current situation, and therefore you are not really a free thinker. And if you think neither way, and this will reveal the Spaniard in his amusing weakness, you outrage both groups." Across the sweetly old-smelling room a girl shouted to a friend, "You must stop thinking about Lorca!"

Luis laughed, a high, delighted child laugh. "Ah, women! I'll tell you. The Spaniard loves—no, adores! and worships!—women. He cannot help himself in their presence. When an Englishman sees a woman cross her legs, he puts a newspaper before his face. When the Frenchman sees, he leers, because he is mechanically trying to live up to the reputation the French have for l'amour. But the Spaniard, when he sees this divine gesture, a fire roars in him, and he wants to leap at her. Women from all over the world, especially your America, come to Spain to feel feminine. They return to their own country with sadness but with a new warmth."

At the table next to us a young man with thick black sideburns was reading an English newspaper. I caught the headlines of one story, about a workers' strike in the north of Spain, and arrests.

Luis must have read my mind. He tapped me on the hand affectionately. "It is so stupid for this government to throw people out who say things against it. So stupid. It just gives the press an opportunity to say Spain is fascist. Why, why are those officials so frightened and stupid?" He inhaled his beloved strong cigarette. "After Franco, it will be a monarchy, and this is just as well. The monarchy—that boy Franco is preparing is perfectly harmless, nice, not a 'jet-setter,' you know, and he has no ideas that could bother himself or anyone else—will simply be a neutral abstraction, not at all a political organism, because, thank the Lord, the monarchists are beginning to think with their heads for a change. It will be a bridge between realities, while the real political parties collect themselves, organize their power and their goals. A Christian democracy, perhaps. Part socialist, maybe. Communism in Spain? Ah, that is a long and complicated story, too complicated for the newness of our friendship." He made a wry face and put out his cigarette. "Besides, politics is for people without souls. It gives them the illusion of creating something."

I glanced around the café. A slope-shouldered boy with a soft face was telling the fat waiter a joke. In a corner a lark-eyed girl was dreamily eating roasted almonds and reading a book of French poetry.

"The terrible problem in Spain," Luis continued, his voice now a little deeper, "has always been that a few people had everything and the rest of us had nothing, but each other. Now that has changed, and I hope it will continue to change. There is not as much despair, you see." He smiled, a young, poetic smile. "When all is said and done, the Spanish people just want to live like everyone else. Do you understand?" I said I did. He put his small hand on my shoulder. "Let me finish telling you about being an intellectual, because it is possible this will help you in your pursuit of Spain. The life of the intellectual must be a quiet one. He cannot move around much. That is for silly people who think they will find themselves somewhere else. All of the places he has to go are in his head. His needs are simple. A couple of friends, his family, and his pencil." I looked out the window. At that moment, two members of the Civil Guard passed, their ominous black patent-leather hats cutting off my view.

> *"You absolutely must try the Serrano ham,"* *the Princess said, spearing a slice. "It is exquisite, so much superior to the Italian variety. Joselito, you are making a glutton of me, you know that, don't you?"*
> *The host grinned. "Life is so beautiful when you are with friends."*

We were driving through the dry, blowy farmlands of Castile, north of Madrid, the sixteenth-century spires of Segovia disappearing in the chilly distance behind us and the gaunt blue sky staring us down. The farm hands, elegant with their expressions of infinite durability, were idling in the tight sun, leaning against a house wall. I asked them how things were.

"Oh, they are quite all right, sir, quite all right," replied a heavy-shouldered man in blue overalls, and he looked quickly around at the others.

"Oh?" I said, surprised, because I had heard otherwise.

"What I mean is," he went on, sensing my disbelief, "things are much better than they were. Oh yes."

"How were they?"

"Very bad." The wind was driving dust all around us. "For a few years there was nothing. It was very difficult. Farming is never easy, even when things are not bad."

"Why do you stay here?"

He looked at me as though I were peculiar. "Because I was born here."

I turned to a lean, amused young man who was wearing his black beret at an angle, and asked him about his situation.

"I like it here," he said, smiling at the others as if to ask their forgiveness for what he was going to say, "but I would not mind going to work in a factory." The other men chuckled with some awkwardness at this. "Oh, I know that it would not be so friendly as here, but the money, that is one thing there would be more of. And my family could live a little better."

I asked him if he wanted his children to become farmers.

"Yes," he said, slowly, a more serious look coming over his face. "If they want to. It will be their choice, not mine. I am not the kind of father who tells his children what kind of life they must have." He looked out over the deeply plowed fields where a solitary mule was standing. "One feels close to people here. We do not think of politics in the city, that kind of thing. No. That is not for us."

"To learn a trade could be something good," an old man with a scar on his hand said almost to himself.

Small in the simple sky above us, a black bird glided and dropped, and soared up suddenly, and glided again, giving the emptiness an indescribable meaning.

In a tiny, tiled room in a house in that chilly dust-swept village I sat on a hard wood chair and sipped the local sweet wine and talked to a solid young woman with porcelain-blue eyes. "I was studying to be a nurse in Segovia," she told me, looking right into my heart, "but I got sick and had to come back to my village, to my parents' house."

I searched her hands for a wedding ring, but none was there. On the blanched wall across the dirt road were painted the words TODOS POR LA PATRIA. I asked this clear-faced young woman why she wanted to leave the village in the first place.

"To become something," she said. "The life here is simple and pleasant, but I would like it to be more rich. My own life, that is. I would like to go back and finish schooling, but I am not so sure that I am not too old." She was twenty-five.

I asked her if she could tell me about the women in Spain. What they felt and wanted, if anything. The women in such villages.

"If they are like me, I can." She smiled with her honest eyes. "I would like to have more culture, then I could understand problems better. One is treated well as a woman, with respect of course, but I feel that the life is not big enough. I think all women in Spain want this bigger life for themselves. Do I express myself right?"

I assured her that she did. Her mother very properly, and with some insistence, offered me an anisette cooky to munch with the pale amber wine. On the wall was a picture of the Virgin Mary.

In a half-deserted street in Vitoria a boy in short pants was making imaginary passes at the bull. He taunted it with sharp cries. Another little boy came up. "You will never make it," he said.

"Not while you're here anyway," the other said, and swirled the invisible cape to trick the charging black bull.

The government official leaned back in his mahogany swivel chair, held the lapel of his gray chalk-striped suit, and, in precise, British-accented English, said, "One can't trust the press. It is irresponsible and terribly prejudiced."

What is the morale in Spain today?

"High, and getting higher all the time. We finally have a sound economy and we want to give the people more of the good things. Improve the level of living in the lower classes."

Can you enumerate some of Spain's problems?

"Reform in the agrarian structure, that must come about very soon if we are to overcome unemployment of farm workers. At present, the workers are not properly distributed at the right time and seasons. This affects the entire agricultural situation. Then, of course, there is a certain amount of discontent in some factories, strikes, for money and more voice, but that will be taken care of by the government."

Would you say the workers' strikes have social implications?

"Some of their problems are authentic, some are not. If their protests have an authentic basis, then they are not really problems, wouldn't you agree? Then, of course, the socialists and Communists are trying to infiltrate their ranks in order to exploit them politically. This is a bad thing."

Do you think Spain could ever become a democracy?

"Ah, that depends on what you mean by democracy. We could not have an Anglo-Saxon democracy, because we do not discriminate against race or color. Ha, ha. That was a sort of joke. Seriously, we cannot find non-Spanish solutions for Spanish problems. It would be a disgrace to squeeze her into a foreign pattern. I can foresee, perhaps, a kind of limited democracy here. Qualified and limited."

Why isn't there political freedom in Spain?

"I don't feel any limitation on my political expression here. It is merely that we do not have the usual Anglo-Saxon channels of so-called political freedom. I find it extremely easy to think as I please. The fact that we do not have popular elections does not change or limit my political thought. Do you see? Always Spain is being measured by foreign measurements. This is absurd. Americans are always telling me how great their own political freedom is. But I do not believe this. Any student of the American scene, which I have been, will tell you that the very illusion of political freedom in America makes it easier to manipulate the masses, in a quite insidious way, than it is to dictate to the masses here. A Spaniard may be ordered to do something, but he cannot be tricked. Quite a difference, don't you agree?"

What sort of party do you feel would result from a completely free election?

"Socialist. It is the only really organized party on a mass level. And of course the Communists would attempt to use this fact to gain power, in one way or another. That is why there is no free election. The Communist party is highly intelligent, highly trained, persistent, and financially well backed. Very clever, those French-trained chaps with the squinty eyes and the thick glasses. They love to have other people sing the 'International' because they themselves can't carry a tune."

Can you tell me what you feel are some of the common misconceptions about Spain, abroad, that is?

"Yes. That Spain is a fascist country. That Africa starts at the Pyrenees. That Spaniards are unable to live a life of their own. All rubbish. For some reason, Spain brings out the anger and fantasy of other countries. I sometimes think that the big powers are furious at us because we do not want power as they do. This seems an unnatural and punishable thing to them. As for privacy, the Spaniard's privacy is a real one, and not a myth he learned in school. And because he has real privacy, it is possible for him to be truly intimate with someone, that is, share his privacy. Intimacy is not possible in your country because your people have so many illusions, poor substitutes for privacy."

Can you tell me what the university students are demonstrating about?

They don't really know themselves. But a protesting youth is a healthy sign. If you find out what they want, I wish you would tell me. I suspect it is just part of being intellectual—to protest means to think, to paraphrase Descartes. Seriously, a very small part of the student body is antiregime. They are being educated by this government. If they don't like it, why do they accept its hospitality? Also, the demonstrations are organized by a small, small group of politically minded people. They are exploiting the exuberance of the students. I fear they will go on, however, until they have themselves a dead martyr. That would delight them."

How do you feel about the accusations that the government here suppresses the people?

"I would precisely say that Franco knows exactly what the Spaniard wants, what is good for him. He is a great moderator of the various Spanish impulses, if you may. He has never been a doctrinaire, never forced his opinions on the public. He has rounded the Spaniards up and now leads them. Now you cannot do that to a suppressed people, can you? You cannot push the Spaniard. He will give you everything, but voluntarily. Pressure only stiffens him. Restrictions under the Franco government have never been tyrannical. This has been a dictatorship, yes, but not a totalitarian state. They are totally different things, wouldn't you say?"

He got up and straightened his polka-dot tie and brushed imaginary particles from his jacket. "Now let us get something to eat. I know a splendid place where we can get suckling pig. A Spanish specialty."

The white-haired old man sitting in the delicate park in Burgos was reading a newspaper. "Look! The face of El Cordobes on the front page again. A bullfighter on the front page. What an idea!"

"Can you think of a better one?" a young man in an old leather jacket said. His eyes looked quite far away. He was blind.

The gray-uniformed police were all over the streets near the American Embassy in Madrid. Standing in doorways and on all the street corners and even mingling with the crowds in the bars. Next to their pistols on their right sides hung the long leather-covered truncheons. Sitting alertly in their new beige jeeps—steel-topped and looking like arrogant bugs—were the riot police wearing white steel helmets. They were all waiting in the twilight for the students' demonstration against American intervention in Vietnam. The tension in the air made my skin feel dirty. The students were strolling casually in twos and threes up and down the Avenida del Generalissimo and the side streets. They were casually dressed and relaxed. Their hair was happily undisciplined. The police just stared at them stiffly, but the many secret service men, all in raincoats, it seemed, examined their faces carefully for future incrimination.

"Why are they doing this to me?" a swollen, muggy cop said to his mate in the doorway. "My God! Must they always be upsetting things?"

My newspaper friend said, "At the last demonstration I attended, the cops beat up several of the kids and arrested half a dozen or so. And they smashed a photographer's camera." He nodded to a passing student. "You've got to admire the kids. They've really got guts."

The traffic was honking and screeching, and the numbers of strolling students had increased. "You notice the kids aren't bunching up," my friend said. "They've adopted guerrilla tactics. The cops would like to meet them head on, like in a movie battle scene."

We were stopped on a corner by two thick-faced policemen. "The street is barred to pedestrians," one said firmly.

"We're newspapermen," Walters said, and showed his press card.

The policeman wearily waved us on, his disgust undisguised. We passed two secret service men who looked us up and down. One of them had an uncontrollable eye twitch. At all the corners now pedestrians were being told by the cops they could not go into the side streets. Now for the first time even the pedestrians looked nervous. A bearded young student with a scarf over his shoulder hurried by us. "On the Calle Galgada," he whispered, thinking we were participants.

Walters touched my arm. "Look," he said, pointing to a black car across the street. "A secret service guy with a long-range camera. Jesus. The pictures he takes will also go to the American Embassy and the CIA. They all want to believe this is being organized by Communist sympathizers."

Suddenly, from the deceptive, passive shadows, about fifty students materialized into a group in the middle of the street. "Johnson assassin! Johnson assassin!" They chanted and began stopping all the cars, leaning on them, standing in front of them. The honking was mad.

"Johnson is a criminal! Johnson is a criminal!" The strange thing was that none of the drivers protested. Something silenced them. Walters and I ran along the streets with groups of kids. The scene was frantic now. Cars were backed up for blocks, honking in frenzy. A motorcycle cop drove around as in a dream. "Ho Chi Minh! Ho Chi Minh!" The kids shouted, weaving in and out of the cars.

"The same dirty little tramps!" shouted a well-dressed boy surrounded by other well-dressed boys.

"You fascist bastard!" a long-haired girl demonstrator shouted back.

"Leave Vietnam in peace! Leave Vietnam in peace!"

From down at the corner a student came running. "The cops! The cops!" and the kids swiftly broke up and began running down a dark side street. Now the cops came, pounding heavily. I was almost knocked over by one of them who was cursing, "Goddamn them! Goddamn them!" More cops were pounding up from their waiting posts, but the kids were far away down the side streets. We ran after them. "They're driving the cops nuts," Walters said, in delight.

People were watching from all the windows. A bloated-faced woman in an apron yelled to the running, panting cops, "Hit them in the heads. They have too much hair!" The kids were safely in the distance of the winding old street.

"They're beautiful," said Walters, as we ran along. "Just beautiful."

Again, as if they had sprung from someone's dream, another bunch of kids formed at an intersection to our left, stopping the cars and shouting, "Leave Vietnam in peace! Criminals!" In the half-darkness and bathed by the automobile headlights, they seemed like actors in an eerie play. Now, far down that street, the cops began to run toward them.

"It's true what they say," a woman behind me said to her amazed husband. "It's true."

Something new appeared on the scene—the jeeps with the riot cops in their steel helmets spilling out, and waving their long black truncheons.

My mouth was dry, from running, and the taste on my tongue was like blood. The sound of their heavy boots seemed to be pounding on my body.

Back on the main street a few minutes later we came upon a man being forcibly escorted to a car by two secret service men. The man was in a panic. "Charlie! Charlie!" he shouted, about to cry. "Help me, for God's sake! I haven't done anything. Please help me. I don't want them to beat me up! Oh, please!"

Walters, shaking his head at the hysteria of the man, went over and talked to the police, who had by now thrust him into the back seat of the car. It seemed the man had gone into a church to change the tape on his recording machine—he was a sort of correspondent —at his own risk because he knew this was not allowed, to record such things, and a completely puzzled priest had called the police. The man was sweating in terror. I had to turn away.

Later on the police arrested fourteen students and carried them to jail in the black police wagon. In front of me the American Embassy looked like a stuffy crocked old lady.

> *In El Greco's brooding Toledo, in the modest square in front of his tortured cathedral, I was approached by a red-shawled woman beggar. "I thought begging was against the law?" I said to my Spanish friend, after giving the woman some coins.*
>
> *"It is," he said.*
>
> *"How do you explain her then?"*
>
> *He shrugged. "She must be a rebel."*

D riving into the dark green hills of the Basque country was a sensual joy. The sharp, clean air made my face tingle, the blue of the sky was oh, so blue and sure of itself, and the herds of sheep and cattle and the ruddy-faced people around them clearly shared a rich and natural oneness. Nowhere did I sense the splitting angles of conflict. I had come to see the University of Pamplona and to talk with a member of the Opus Dei, the Catholic lay-men's organization that so many people have interpreted in so many ways within the context of Spain's contorted destiny.

This trimly barbered, chubby-cheeked, nattily dressed man and I met in a hotel lobby facing one of the close, twisting streets where the frightened, angry bulls are turned loose once a year at festival time. I could clearly hear them in my mind as they clattered wildly down the streets as the young men ran and shouted in delight and terror.

Would smiling, successful Señor Clavel please tell me what the Opus Dei is?

"It is a Christian lay order whose members are dedicated to sanctifying themselves through their work."

Is it in any way a political organization?

He gave me an expression that is usually reserved for misguided children. "Is God political? No, the Opus Dei is not, no matter what the accusations have been from all sides. Its members have their own political views, left, right, center. Some are even members of the Falange. I did not dedicate my life to a political organization. That would be degrading."

What does the Opus Dei do in the community?

"Everything any good Christian would do in living

the gospel of Christ. Members of Opus Dei have built schools, hospitals, camps, clinics, things like that, all over the world. Africa, even America. Life is more rewarding if one improves it. We believe in raising the human standard wherever it is possible. And not only among Catholics."

Do the members take orders, or directions, from the Opus Dei headquarters in Rome?

"No, no orders are given to anyone. Everything is voluntary. When we are told that a project is being started, or that one should be started in a needy area, we can contribute if we like. Also, all of our projects, like the University of Pamplona, benefit from local and government aid."

Are members ever told to band together in other than a philanthropic and spiritual way?

"Absolutely not." Another look of compassionate pain came over his otherwise unclouded face. "You know, I often feel that outsiders attribute to us their own failings and fantasies about themselves. Plotters accuse us of plotting, underground people accuse us of being underground, fascists accuse us of having power dreams. All nonsense. Each person does what his heart dictates from a Christian motivation."

It is said that when Franco dies, or when he ceases to function, that the Opus Dei, as an arm of the Church, will fill the void.

"Another projection by those who have always been anti-Church."

It is said that Opus Dei members form a professional elite and because of being Opus Dei get the best jobs.

"A minority of us are professionals. The majority are from the general middle class and from the lower classes, so-called. People think we are a trained elite merely because such members naturally are apt to come to public attention more often. Now, the other thing is logical. It is not that Opus Dei people are favored over others, *ipso facto*. If they get a promotion or position it is because they happen to be best qualified for it."

Do you as an Opus Dei member—or as yourself—endorse the Franco government, and the things done in the name of the government?

He sighed and looked out into the old street, where one store window was covered with long smoked sausages and heavy cheeses, and when he answered his voice was lower than it had been. "No. Spain needs more freedom, civil rights, human dignity. It is disgusting what the police have done to the striking working class and to the demonstrating students and priests. I am not advocating chaos, mind you, only fewer restrictions, more feeling about the human situation. This is my own personal point of view. I do not speak for the Opus Dei members. They must speak for themselves."

Why did you become a member of Opus Dei?

The deep inner glow in him showed in his eyes and made his mouth lose a certain tightness it possessed. "Before, I felt my life had very little purpose. All I did seemed for immediate and personal satisfaction. Now I have depth and richness and purpose. I now feel that life is sacred. This is what I owe to Opus Dei."

Do your members evangelize?

"We simply tell people of our own joy and happiness and if they respond to what Opus Dei seems to say, they can join. We do not lure others, as some religions do."

How do you feel about atheism, or a society that contends there is no God?

"All I know is that God gives meaning to a community. Without Him there is a terrible materialism."

The future of Spain, what political form will it take?

"Socialism. A humanist socialism. Not Communism."

Do you meet regularly with other members of Opus Dei?

"Oh yes. Once a week. We meet, a small number of us, that is, a priest who is our spiritual adviser. These are purely spiritual meetings, nothing more, nothing less."

Could you synthesize what Opus Dei gives you?

The glow again. "A greater sense of responsibility as a human being." His smile was enveloping me like the morning light.

> *"Isn't it a great pain in the ass to do this army duty?"*
>
> *"Well, it could be," the soldier answered, sipping his red wine, "but I'm plugged in at the right places. That helps a lot."*
>
> *His friend slapped him on the back. "Even in school you knew which teachers to corrupt. What a devil you are, Pedro." In the back of the Madrid bar two young soldiers were playing a slot machine under a color photograph of Dominguín about to put his sword in the bleeding bull.*

I met the prostitute Lala in a chattering, quite un-degraded-looking outdoor café in Málaga. A Spanish friend had told me this was where the elite of the girls were to be found. It was early evening and the clean white iron tables and chairs vibrated softly in the twilight. The people at the tables communicated no shrillness and the couples walking in the street were in a contentment of slow motion.

"Spanish men are so funny," she was saying, as she sipped her vermouth cassis. She was a blonde with black glistening eyes and her simple black dress was cut low, revealing the naked swell of her breasts. She looked like an average good-looking young woman. The only thing that made me think of her being a prostitute, as I looked at her, was her mouth. The expression around its fullness was one of sensual cynicism. "My God! They are so vain and absurd. Like the children of rich people who are brought up by simple little country girls." And she laughed, a heavy, rich laugh that you hear in Elizabethan plays. Two calm-faced middle-class women having a coffee at a table near us stopped talking and looked at us, then looked away. This embarrassed me, but I liked the laughter.

"You know them better than I do," I said. "They seem so *bravo* to me." I was thinking of the way they acted in bars and when they walked along the streets, especially when there was more than one of them.

"Yes," she said, smiling very knowingly, "that is the way they want to seem, very *bravo* and tough and very devilish. But when you close the door"—and she wagged her manicured finger—"it is another story. They are very afraid and nervous like little boys. Or they are mean and rough. I think because they think that is the way a man acts with a woman, to show how big and tough and masterly he is. But I am not fooled by that." She patted at her carefully half-teased hair, and then, for no reason, let one of her hands slowly slide down the softness of her neck.

"And does that bother you, I mean their being rough and unpleasant?" I asked, noticing out of the corner of my eye that the short, very young waiter in a stiff white jacket was standing in the doorway of the café observing us with complete interest.

She grimaced philosophically. "It used to upset me in the beginning, but I got used to it. In Spain everyone gets used to everything." I lit her cigarette, which she put in a silver holder, and then I noticed for the first time that she did not inhale. I wanted to ask her why, but I did not. "I decided it wasn't personal, because, of course, they did not know me. That makes a difference, if you know what I mean." She turned her head slightly and blew the smoke out so that it would not come into my face. "But it's all a little game. That is what they pay for, that little game." Something occurred to her, and she smiled almost secretly as she drank off her vermouth. "I am in the business of the love game. Isn't that funny?"

"I guess it is, in a way," I said, "if it really does amuse you."

She leaned forward, as if she were going to whisper, but her voice remained the same as she talked. "You know, it is not unusual that the men cannot do anything. Not at all. I have had this happen many times to me. A complete washout," and she dropped her hand in the air like a guillotine. "And do you know what they do then?"

"Refuse to pay you?"

"Oh, that has happened too. No. They blame it on

me. Me!" And she pointed a finger into the cleft between her breasts. "Can you imagine such a—such a thing of nonsense? As if I were their mama and I had cooked them such a bad meal they lost their appetite. Oh! They say such silly, silly things when that happens to them. 'You have rushed me and that is bad for me,' or 'Your apartment is too cold. It has frozen my feelings.' My apartment is lovely and warm, mind you. One, not so long ago, either, a fat fellow with smelly pomade on his hair, said something that I just had to laugh out loud at. He said, 'I just remembered. Your name is the same as my sister's, and I have always been afraid I wanted to make love to my sister.' Oh my Lord!" And again she laughed that dark, lovely way. "Some of the washouts have been drinking too much," she continued, blowing the smoke away again, puffing her cheeks a little as she did. "That makes them feel like tigers in their head but bad elsewhere." She looked at me closely. "You don't drink too much, do you?"

"No," I told her. "A little bit goes a long way with me."

"That's good. Listen. Let's take a little walk, eh? I have a fear that my legs will get fat if I sit too much," and she reached over and pinched my cheek. "You are nice, do you know that? It's good to be with a man who is not a Spaniard."

After we had been walking a few yards—the air of the night now tasted palely of the sea and quite far away a ship sounded its deep-throated warning—she said, "I am almost always walking alone. This is a different thing for me."

"Don't you get lonely?" I asked her.

"When I was a little girl my father told me that

everyone was lonely and that I should not worry my-self about it." A little boy in a long white apron rushed by us carrying a large bunch of roses. His face was very serious. "And I have learned that he knew what he was saying."

"What did your father do?" I asked. I had always wondered about the fathers of prostitutes, thinking, quite innocently, that they could not be like other fa-thers.

"Oh, he was just a little clerk in a bank. He spent his life counting other people's money." She paused for a moment in her talking, as if she were picturing what she was saying. "I think that would make me very angry, don't you think so?"

"Yes. It could make you feel strange. Maybe it could even make you tired of money."

She laughed a little. "You are funny. I like you. Does it make you nervous walking with me?"

"No," I said, not telling the whole truth. I had never taken a stroll with a prostitute before.

"We can hold hands if you like. The people might think I am your girl friend," and she took my hand in hers. "Do you have a girl friend?"

"I'm just getting a divorce."

She looked at me with surprise and sympathy. "Oh. I am very sorry."

"Don't be. It's really a good thing. I don't feel bad."

"How sad it is to end a marriage. It is supposed to be a sacred thing." An old taxi roared in front of us as we crossed the street, and the driver said something about people who close their eyes when they step off a curb. We headed toward a little park where a foun-tain was making sad strangling noises. "My mother was always criticizing my father," she said. "She was sorry she married him. She had a little tobacco shop, but she didn't like it." She looked at me and smiled. "I don't think he liked to make love to her. She was talking all the time."

"Did you like your father?"

"I guess so. I felt sorry for him. He lost a leg in that lousy war."

The park was dark and quiet, except for the strangling sound, and it seemed somehow like a place to hide. It did not ask you any questions. It was thinking about itself. The only other people there were two old men in berets. They were making sporadic old-man talk. The stillness of the park was so sensitive that Lala's perfume was like another presence there.

"It's very nice here," I said, lighting a cigarette.

She looked at me closely through the self-possessed darkness. "Are you unhappy?"

"No. Why do you ask?"

"Oh, I don't know. You seem to be thinking all the time."

This time I laughed. She was quite different from other professionals I had chanced to talk to. I was thinking about her father's lost leg, when she suddenly said, in a voice much lighter and higher now, a voice almost of her childhood, "Would you like to hear a little game I play when I am in bed with the men?"

"Uh, sure. Tell me."

Smiling that special way of a child who is doing something different, and looking quickly over at the two old men, to be sure, I suppose, that they had not moved closer, she said, "Well, I imagine that I am someone else. All kinds of different women. The wife of Hernández the baker, the wife of Alfau who owns the wine shop, or the big-breasted wife of the mean man who owns the building I live in. It's a very amusing game, and I made it up."

"It's certainly unusual," I said, really in surprise. "Have you always done this? I mean since you, uh, became . . ."

"A couple of years ago. I was with an army officer—oh, he was so bald!—and he wanted me to spank him. Like a bad boy, he said. I had never done that before—I have done a lot of funny things but not that one, you see—I had never spanked anyone in my life. At first I just could not think of myself doing it. Then I thought, well, you saw Mrs. Ortega spanking her nasty son Felipe that day in the park, so I imagined that I was Mrs. Ortega, and with her mean little eyes, and I began to say the things I remembered she had said to little Felipe, and I gave it to the army officer real good. It worked very well, then after that I began thinking I was other married women who live in my neighborhood. Doesn't that make you laugh! What do you think they would say if they knew what they were doing every night in my apartment? Oh Lord! Those proper ladies."

"Very. I've never heard of that one before."

"The army officer came to see me once a week to get his spanking. But you know, whenever I would see him in the street when I was walking, he would not say hello to me. Oh well. The man who is at the bar of the Café Fornos told me that he was in charge of a prison during the war and he used to do terrible things to the prisoners. What a person!"

Two grim-faced Civil Guardsmen strolled into the park, walking close together, each one with a hand casually resting in his gun belt, and routinely looked through the park. They looked us over with an official indifference, and walked on, their hard leather heels making cold sharp sounds on the cement. For a moment they made me feel guilty and afraid. A church bell tolled the time, and the enormous metal sound made the park seem fragile and tiny.

"Do you mind the police?" I asked, my voice involuntarily lowering itself.

"No. They never bother me. They are just simple men doing their stupid jobs . . . like everyone else."

I finally asked her the child's question that had been on my mind all evening, perhaps all my life. "Why is it that you seem so different? I mean, how come you . . ."

She laughed and slapped my knee twice as if to reprimand me. "I think you see too many bad movies in America. Why do people think that all prostitutes must be very vulgar or very stupid? We can be like anyone else. This is just a business. Do you understand?"

"I guess it's difficult for me to see it that way," I confessed.

She turned and faced me and put her hand on my knee. "Listen to me. I went to school and I read books and I became a secretary after going to a business school. In both places that I worked I discovered that I had to sleep with the boss if I wanted to keep my job. You see? Then I got married because I was sick of that, and I discovered that all my husband really wanted me for was to be in the bed. He went out with his friends when he wanted amusement and friendship. I was a prisoner of the bed and I was not getting more than my room and board, so to speak. So I said to myself, Lala, this is dreadful. If that is all men want you for then you should get paid for it and then you will be your own boss like the head of any business and do what you want. So here I am. And it is really no different from that other. But now I get paid. And I do not have to scrub floors or listen to a man complaining all the time. That gives me a terrible headache. Now you have my story." And she smiled and pinched my cheek. "Yes?"

"The whole thing sounds very reasonable. I have heard many women say the same complaints but they did nothing about it."

"Then I pity them." She took my hand and stood up. "I'm getting chilly. Let's go to my place. All right?"

"Okay."

As we walked out of the guileless park, leaving the two old soliloquists, I said jokingly, "Who will you be tonight?"

"What? Oh, that!" She laughed. "I don't know yet. Maybe," and she took my arm, "maybe I will be myself."

On the white chest in her living room was a ten-cent-store framed photograph of President Kennedy.

The little girls were skipping-walking down the leaky gray street in Bilbao. They had their arms around each other's waist. "Tomorrow when I go to school," the taller one said, "Sister Margaret will say, 'Angelina, you have learned your lessons very well. I will reward you. You do not have to do any homework for two days.' "

"I wish that would happen to me," said the other.

"My mother is very nice to me when I am good like that."

A desolate black dog trotted lamely in front of them. The smaller girl kicked at it, and it ran whimpering into an alley.

The four workers and a priest and I were sitting tensely in a small bare room in the rectory of a church in a poor section of Barcelona. We were meeting secretly because these men were of the illegal underground workers' union whose members were constantly fighting the government suppression of a free labor movement. We were all slightly nervous; the government had spies all over, and we could all go to jail for this meeting. The dark night outside, jostled by occasional church bells, completed the aura of conspiracy.

"For a while," one was saying, a strong-faced boy who was a metal worker, "we thought it would be possible to have a good, free life and feel like meaningful human beings. That was when the government had its spell of liberal dizziness about a year ago. But when we showed how strong we were and how serious we were about our own unions and our bargaining rights, that dream was killed." And he made a sword-chopping gesture with his muscular red hand. "The government returned to its fascist position." He swallowed some cold beer from the bottle.

I asked about the official workers' syndicates. The thin-mouthed, thin-nosed but warm-eyed young priest could not help laughing out loud. "Oh lovely! Yes indeed. The official syndicate takes care of the workers all right. The director of each local is a member of the Falange and dismisses any worker who is suspected of being underground or in any way involved in thoughts or projects of a decent, liberal nature."

An older man, with a heavily lined face and sensitive, hurt eyes, lit a fresh cigarette from the old one, coughed harshly, and then said, "García over there lost his foreman's job just last week because of participating in a workers' demonstration." García shrugged and made a "so what?" face. "Three members of our local committee are in jail right now awaiting trial— their crime being that they want the right to organize their own free unions and determine their own fate, rather than to be a simple-minded puppet in Franco's dictatorship. Sickening. Their families, how will they live while these men are in prison, in prison for all of us? It makes me want to cry, I confess to you." And he coughed heavily and rubbed his sensitive eyes.

"Smoking is bad for your health, Jorge," said the boy Federico jokingly.

"So is being here."

I asked them how they felt about the arrest three days previously of forty-seven of their leaders in the Madrid area, just before a big demonstration was planned. García, a heavy-mouthed man with thick black eyebrows, answered. "For every one those bastards arrest, we will produce twenty more. There is nothing they can do to stop us. We are not afraid of them. They are afraid of us, they know it, and we know it. Their dirty backs are against the wall: we have just begun."

Feeling like an idiot in my innocence and nonparticipant role, I brought up the subject of negotiating directly with the Minister of the Interior in Madrid. The priest shouted "Ha!" in mock amusement. The man who had not spoken yet answered me. He wore a neat cheap suit that had been mended at the cuffs, and he played with his wedding band as he spoke.

"We went all the way to Madrid to see him, but he

would not even open his door to us. We were treated as though we were insane impostors." He smiled and shook his head at the mockery of it. The room was suddenly filled with the tolling of the church bells above our heads. The vibrations brought us all together into a physical unity. I could feel the tolling deep in my veins. "Our movement is growing all the time. The more the police push us, the more we will push back. If they employ violence, so will we. Decency will get them decency. It is like that." He paused and drank a little beer from a glass. The others were totally absorbed in what he was saying: he was saying more than words for them. "The conscience of Spain is on our side." He looked steadily at me, then at the others. "More and more the people of all walks of life are resenting the government. The future is no longer dead."

As if anticipating my question, young Federico began talking very rapidly. "Spain's working classes are united. And we are like brothers with the students and intellectuals. We are in the same fight. It is the middle class who need educating. The little bourgeois and the big bourgeois. Their materialism makes them passive. They can only think now of their own possessions and their own skins. And making money. They think money is God, but this is a degrading confusion. They are basically sympathetic to the cause—you can call it a revolution, if you like—but they are afraid to show it. They have been trained in fear by the Franco government. We must show them that our cause is toward life, not toward chaos and terror." The priest was nodding his head in agreement. Federico reached out his hand for a cigarette from García without taking his eyes from mine. "But we do not kid ourselves. We know that the workers will always be the motor of the social revolution." The room was very smoky now, and through the spiral of García's cigarette smoke I could barely make out the painted blood stains on the small crucifix on the wall behind him.

I said the government had charged last week that the workers' union was Communist-led. This made Jorge spit on the floor in disgust. "They say that about everything that is a protest. That is how they want to discredit us and protest in general. They won't admit to the people that the movement is authentic and local and has nothing to do with communism or politics of any kind." He pointed his finger at me now and spoke slowly and most precisely. "Do you know that we have turned down offers of help, money and people, from Communist-socialist parties in France and Italy because we did not want to be corrupted or used in any way? We wanted any help to be completely unconditional. They wanted us to use their trained organizers. Not that we are against socialism, because we are all probably socialist, but we simply do not want to be told by outsiders, with political interests, how to run our show. We could use the money—for helping families of imprisoned men, men out of jobs, to propagandize—but we turned it down. Do you understand that?"

I asked about the families of the imprisoned workers. The quiet man in the brown suit told me, "They are supported by the voluntary contributions of thousands of workers all over Spain." He smiled. "You know, the women are so marvelous. They are so strong and they are completely behind us. They are worried, of course, but not afraid. You mentioned living standards before. None of the workers' families would be able to live at all decently unless the woman in the family worked also. She might do sewing at home, or make little toys or cheap jewelry. Things like that. And they have their own organizations, the wives of the men workers. They are very strong. At demonstrations they dare the police to charge them with their horses. And more than once, in order to keep us from being clubbed by the police, the women have blocked them with their own bodies."

The church bell suddenly filled the room with its enormous tolling, almost moving us in our seats. The men all looked at their watches. They had to leave; they had to rise at 5 a. m. for their jobs. On the way out, García said to me, "Nothing is going to stop the workers, I can assure you."

I asked him if they would go as far as sabotaging, since their strike efforts have been so futile, seemingly. "We will do whatever is historically necessary," he said, and I knew he was dead serious.

Walking alone with the priest across the moonlit churchyard, the crunching of our shoes on the gravel the only sound there, I said how impressed I had been by the men. "I love them," he said. "They are so courageous, so committed to their principles. They have taught me what it is to be a Christian. Yes, you do not learn about God in a church, my friend."

"I have jars!" the man at the Avila market sang out. "Strong and cheap! Be good to yourself and buy one!"

A bright-faced boy came by pushing a small cart. "Ice cream!" his bell-high voice proclaimed. "Wonderful ice cream! Sweet and cold!"

In the permissive sky above, a Spanish pilot

*in an American jet fighter plane left a thick white
stream of vapor in his ecstatic whistling wake.
The two gray-uniformed policemen on the corner
kept following it, smiling.*

The good-looking, quick-eyed businessman in his
late thirties, wearing an expensive English
Shetland jacket, said, "All that Americans can
talk about is the Black Legend—fascist Spain,
the Monster of the Civil War. Why can't they stop
this nonsense? That was thirty-odd years ago. Spain is
not the same. There is prosperity here and a good life
and people can do what their capacities tell them they
can do. What if there is not political freedom? Is that
the most important thing in life, that ritualistic gesture
of self-determination that is everywhere just a ritual?
The Spanish economy is rising and everybody is happy
about it. We are no longer outcasts. Why is there all
this stupidity of demonstration and riots and anti-
Franco? Do they want the chaos of the Civil War?
They don't realize how clever Franco has been, keeping the country neutral, keeping it from falling into the
hands of the Communists. We have not been in the
war like the others, we are not devastated. Somebody
should tell those fools to stop causing trouble. It is a
damn good thing what the government said—they will
draft the protesting students if they keep up their nonsense. Fun is fun. But enough is enough.

"It is possible to live better in Spain than anywhere
else in Europe, better even than in America. Here it is
possible to belong to oneself instead of to a system, as
it is in England and America. Your power and prosperity are useless. You Americans and English are constantly doing things to prove your existence—always

checking in with the fantastic system that depersonal-
izes you. Not the Spaniard. He is truly a free man. He
knows who he is and what he wants. Oh, there are
some wrong things going on, but it is the same all over
the world. The big thing in Spain is we are out of that
awful depression. We are breathing. We should be
grateful. I can do business with anyone. That is my
kind of freedom," and he tightened the knot in his red-
and-black silk tie for the second time.

> *"Is that a castle?" I asked my friend, a
> Spanish painter, pointing through the small,
> curved leaves of the almond tree toward a light
> gray edifice in the mountains.*
> *"No," he replied, shaking his head. "It is a
> fake with delusions of reality."*

The young student looked like the kids in French
movies—black turtle-neck sweater, long sideburns, hair combed down onto his forehead,
cigarette in the corner of his mouth, smooth-
skinned—a face utterly without a trace of deadness.
Nor were there sly games in his expressions. He was a
member of the student "underground," and meeting
me was risking possible exposure and then police
action.

*What are you and the other kids protesting in the
experience of life in Spain?*

"The whole structure of stupidity and fakery. The
establishment, or the system, has invented a cluster of
myths in order to anesthetize the Spaniard. Soccer,
the bullfight, Church—these myths occupy the people
and effectively prevent them from participating in
reality, their own and their country's. The mass media

here compound the situation by distorting values and giving the people a degraded set to relate to. The newspapers in particular stifle or distort information about their own lives, the lives of their fellow Spaniards. The government wants thick heads and these are sure ways of getting them."

Do you think your activities, the demonstrations and such, are reaching the government at all?

"No question of it. If we weren't seriously bothering those swine, there wouldn't be the repressions and arrests and beatings. They're bothered all right. You see, the Franco people have until now kept the university, and the student body, quite separated from the rest of society. We have been treated like a kind of necessary game, an intellectual abstraction. This is a wonderful way to castrate it, and at the same time to keep your society infantile. The school still gets its official line from the government, plus the official student-body line. Thirty years of paralysis—that is what we must abolish."

Are the student activists representative of the general student body?

"Disgracefully, no. We are a minority. Deep in their hearts the others know what we know, what an awful joke it is, but they are too passive to do anything. They know the system will absorb them, that they will become part of the apparatus, in their jobs and otherwise, and there is nothing they can do about this, unless they are willing to live original lives. However, there has been a gradual and very heartening defection of some of these passive ones over to our activities. Actually, the activists among us feel much closer, more authentic ties with the protesting students in Berke-

ley and elsewhere in America than with the bourgeois kids on our own campus."

*What are your feelings about the older generation
here in Spain?*

"There is no dialogue, no connection really. We feel
we have been given nothing. We have had to invent
ourselves, in a sense. There has been no continuity.
The humanist tradition was broken off so long ago.
The Civil War killed it."

Do you feel the university is really educating you?

"The only valid training it provides is in technology,
the sciences. Other than that it is a joke. The entire
educational system, its values and methods, is dictated
by the bourgeois capitalist society. This is not education, it is manipulative propaganda, molding you to be
a robot member of that society. I'm going there just to
play the lousy game—to get a degree so that I will be
enough accepted in society so that I can make out.
The university aim is to depoliticize us. I get my real
education on the side, reading on my own.

"The entire university system must be reformed. Do
you know, for example, that only one per cent of the
student body comes from the lower classes? This is absurd and incredible. The establishment does not want
the working class to get educated because they would
then overthrow the ruling classes. The school does not
deal with the realities of Spain, it exists in an establishment vacuum. It teaches things that do not relate
to the problems of today. It does not train the students in ideas, just cliché positions. The terrible and
frustrating thing is that the students are prevented
from taking an active part in the university life, in
helping determine their own experience and destiny.

The structure of the experience is forced on us from above."

Is the faculty behind you—that is, behind the student revolt?

"What a laugh! The faculty has abandoned us. They are active nothings. Finks. Our reality menaces their disengagement. One of the professors who actively sympathized with us was thrown out by the government."

The Spanish newspapers are always saying that the underground is run by Communists. Is this true?

"Another of their crummy lies. They blame every protest movement on the Communists. This helps to blind the people, and themselves, to the fact that the protests are authentically, organically our own, and are responses—nonpolitical responses—to very real problems in our country. Another thing about the crummy government—they have paid informers in the student body who keep them informed of all our plans. Them and the American Embassy and the CIA. The pay is three hundred dollars a year. The awful thing is we have not been able to find out who they are."

How do you regard the Church in Spain?

"It has done all it can to immobilize the masses. It is truly one of the causes of the Spanish tragedy. You see, in order to survive, it has had to go along with the fascist government, and consequently it has resisted all forms of change. And it has always been tied to the elite."

What do you feel about the United States?

"The richest, most powerful country in the world has become a monster of intervention and suppression. Its war against the people of Vietnam is loathsome. It is a menace to any indigenous social revolution anywhere in the world. Wait until you see what it will do next in Africa."

Who are some of the people whose work and thinking you admire?

"Walt Whitman, Allen Ginsberg, Jean-Paul Sartre, Marx and Lenin, Pablo Neruda, Quasimodo, Bertrand Russell, Ho Chi Minh, Castro, Yevtushenko, James Joyce. People of quality."

From out in the street came the sound of hands clapping. Someone was summoning the night watchman to open the locked door. It was quite late. The student observed me carefully. He wanted to be sure I had understood him. Like so many underground people in Spain, he had reason to distrust the press. I smiled to reassure him.

> *At the bullfight, the irritated pretty girl turned to her boy friend. "Oh! What a lazy stupid bull! It just stands there."*
>
> *He laughed. "He is trying to figure things out."*
>
> *"But there is nothing to figure out. He is going to die."*
>
> *The crowd began to hiss and to shout bad things at the bull.*

One quiet, shimmering afternoon I went to see a young lay priest who lived with his mother amidst the lyrical innocence of azaleas and palm trees on the outskirts of Barcelona. The young priest, whose face was as clear and sharp as a maxim by Voltaire, was one of the leaders of the Spanish priests' revolution and totally committed to liberal reform on all levels. He sipped a brandy and I smoked an American cigarette as we talked. On the walls of his book-guarded study were pictures of St. Thomas Aquinas and Friedrich Nietzsche.

"I will give you an example, an epiphany if you like, of how numbed the masses are to their own lives here," he said, smiling sadly. "Just the other day I went on a sort of picnic with some workers' children. We were having a good time and I was teaching them some protest songs. You know, things like 'We Shall Overcome.' One of the girls sang it perfectly. But when she had finished she said to me, 'But Father, I have nothing to protest in my life!' The government could not ask for greater ignorance and passivity." He shook his head. "To be so young and sweet and so corrupted."

I asked him what the general feeling was among the workers' families regarding the priests' efforts on their part.

"We work for the workers without the workers," he replied. "They are so exhausted by their work—ten, twelve hours a day six days a week—that they do not want to think. All they want to do is watch television. American cowboy movies, gangster movies, and the inevitable bullfights. They suffer us, these poor people. They smile and say yes to us because they feel sorry for us. It is so pathetic. They do not belong to themselves. They belong to the myths that manipulate them. The government wants empty minds in the people. I'm afraid it has them."

His handsome, graying mother softly came into the room, put some fresh black coffee before me, and, smiling, left without a word. I asked Father M., who teaches philosophy and tutors college students for a living, if the priests' movement had any political point of view.

"No," he said, "not as it would be generally understood. Our revolution is a matter of humanist conscience. It has nothing to do with theology or political parties. We feel that any political party is all right as long as it respects human rights. Communist, socialist, capitalist, it doesn't matter."

I expressed my curiosity about the specific ways he and his fellow worker priests are involved in the workers' underground in the Catalan region. "We arrange for them to hold their secret meetings in the churches, at least fifty in this area alone. The church is the only place where they can meet in safety, without being spied upon or arrested. The police are forbidden by law to enter a church. Then we help them administer their affairs, advise them on their strategy, and some of us aid them in printing and distributing their posters and pamphlets. And we instruct them in birth control," he added with a wink.

I had read so much badly presented information about the priests' revolution in the newspapers that I begged him to illuminate my confusion. He was very amused and reached over and slapped me on the shoulder.

"I like your confusion," he said. "Well, in essence, the new priests are rebelling against the deadness of the Church, or its separation from the human interests of the people it is supposed to serve. Generally, it has been an instrument of the state. The bishops, appointed by the government, have really been government employees, carrying out the dictates of the Franco government, not the idea of God. Just look at the groveling priests in parliament! They help keep the people down. The priests' revolution is aimed toward not only freeing the people but freeing the priests themselves from this suppression. In every way possible on every level."

I brought up the question of the Church's feeling about their activities. "Oh"—he laughed—"the Church does not like us at all! We are always being told to stop our nonsense, to behave like good, obedient priests. But we do not heed them. We tell the bishops what to do. They do not frighten us. We are growing larger and stronger. I spend much time traveling throughout Spain recruiting and organizing my fellow priests into the revolution." He paused to taste the brandy and light a cigarette. "What the Church has forgotten is that the gospels are about human rights. They are not philosophic rituals. And it goes without saying that the government is outraged by our behavior. And it is doing things in desperation that it has never done before—the police are arresting priests for participating in workers' demonstrations, and harassing them whenever possible. They no longer have respect for the office of the priest. Consequently, we will not treat them with respect."

The telephone rang, and Father M. sprang to it. His intense conversation was apparently with another secular priest. In a few moments he hung up. "That was a friend at the Capuchin monastery. He tells me the secret police are keeping them under constant watch. Things look very ugly."

I finished the strong, fragrant black coffee and resumed my search for illumination. Father M.'s directness and honesty gave even the smallest word and gesture resonance and meaning.

"The new priest, the lay or working priests," he went on, gazing in the direction of Thomas Aquinas, "feel they should be like other men, and assume the daily responsibilities of the ordinary man. That is why we work and support ourselves, each in his own capacity. We feel that to be supported by the Church is a form of bondage. We have truck drivers and teachers, laborers and translators among us. We know that God does not live in the cathedral. He lives in us and we carry Him with us. God is life, not the sound of a church bell. We feel that those priests who wish to marry should be allowed to do so. This celibacy is very hard on some men, not so hard on others. Also, it makes one lie to oneself at times.

"What is encouraging," he said, "is that some of the middle class, among them business people, sympathize with this social revolution and even contribute money to it, secretly of course. The bourgeois here want a new life, a free and dynamic life. They want to grow. And on the simplest material level, they know that the Franco type of government must go because, among other things, it is keeping Spain from the Common Market and alienating them from economic prosperity. You can see how nothing is untouched by a bad idea."

There was an urgent knock on the door, and a rushed-looking young man came in. He began rapidly to inform Father M. of the latest police harassment problems. Even the mail of many of the involved priests was being opened in the post office, he said. I thought this was a good time to take my departure. I could not help noticing the lovely purple morning glories just outside his window. They distracted me momentarily from thinking of the immaculate brutality of the suppression machine. I wished Father M. and his friends all the success in the world.

The next day I went to see a young secular priest who lived among the poor on an exhausted hillside on the outskirts of Barcelona. The families were from the south of Spain, where they had lived in an infinity of heat and barrenness and empty dreams.

"They are very good people," the priest told me as we slogged up the muddy road in their dismal "village." "The men work very hard as laborers and they bring home, oh, maybe ten dollars a week. They sometimes drink too much and beat their women, but it is not hard to understand why they do these angry things. The world has sinned against them."

This brooding-cheeked man was truly a poem: there was not a pause of excess about him, and his music, which swirled in and down, not outside, told me more about myself than I had planned for.

Several short, heavy-legged women were walking slowly up the road ahead of us, carrying long loaves of bread and bulging string bags of cheap green vegetables. Over to our right, next to a stained white plaster house that was gradually crumbling away, two young girls were filling plastic containers with water from a hydrant. One of them waved gaily to the priest. To our left, in a garbage-strewn clearing in front of a tiny grocery shop, a toothless old woman in black played with a baby who was chewing on a carrot stub. The women a few feet ahead of us were talking rapidly as they walked. They were dressed cleanly but shabbily.

The priest chuckled. "One of their favorite subjects of conversation is their husbands. They have the most elaborate fantasies about their extramarital doings. I think this amuses them. Deep down of course they know the men really are faithful. They work too hard to be anything else."

A serious-faced boy with circles under his eyes passed us pushing his bicycle. He greeted the priest, but his face did not change into the usual smile. He bowed his head as he pushed on.

"He is a splendid boy," the priest said. "There is a deep strength in him and he is so very young. He refuses to give up to futility. He is an apprentice to an electrician, and he works ten hours a day for, I think, about five dollars a week which, of course, he gives to his family."

I asked him how he went about sustaining their belief in God. As I waited for his answer I watched a man who was reading a newspaper in an old car with no wheels that was clinging to the side of the mountain.

"You do not talk to them about God," the priest finally replied. "That would be too much of an absurd luxury. You talk to them about their daily lives and try to say something meaningful to them on that level." He stepped over a broken toy. "You try to give them a belief in a better future. It is very difficult. The government has abandoned them completely. They get nothing in help, nothing at all."

He excused himself and walked quietly over to a sad-looking young woman who was standing in the doorway of a small white house with a tin roof. A brown bony mongrel padded by me and disappeared through a scarred half-open door. I looked around at the small desolate houses and I could not help feeling that a strong rain would wash them all down the hillside. The priest returned in a few minutes and we walked on toward his little house.

"That poor woman," he said. "She does not know what to do. Her husband was arrested last week in the demonstration against government oppression and no one knows when he will be let out of jail. They could keep him there for a very long time and in the meantime his family can starve. Oh my Lord! What can one do? What can one do?"

I could not think of anything to say. I felt thick with stupidity and frustration. We reached his house and sat down to rest in the cold living room that had two chairs and a tiny table. The whole place had a monastic stare of self-denial and purity. He gave me a cooky and a glass of light white wine. A crucifix hung imploringly on a wall behind the young priest.

I asked him if it did not get lonely for him here among these people who, while they were admirable and made one feel totally human, did not really speak the language of his educated background.

"Oh, yes," he told me, smiling a young tired smile. "It is indeed very lonely here. I miss good conversation and the wine of the intellect. But I see my fellow worker priests a couple of times a week and that makes me feel better. To be surrounded by so much suffering and poverty, so much despair, makes one feel hungry and tired." He shrugged. "But it is my work of God. They need me." He laughed weakly. "I need them. Without such people and one's response to them, Christ does not exist, I can assure you." He looked down at his strong young hands and smiled sadly. At that moment I wanted to put my arms around him and give him whatever I had inside me that would warm him and make him feel better. But I had been trained all my Protestant life not to make such emotional gestures, and I forced the feeling away.

Now he looked up at me and his face had a sudden light in it. "Do you know the poetry of Rilke?"

I told him that I did to a limited extent.

He jumped up. "Let me show you something so lovely that I was reading last night before going to sleep."

Light as a leaf, he spun away into his cramped bedroom and returned with a book of Rilke's poetry. He turned through the pages, found what he wanted, and began to read. "Why do you not think of him / As the coming one, / Imminent from All Eternity / The future one, / The final fruit of a tree whose leaves we are? / What keeps you from projecting / His birth into times / That are in process of becoming, / And living your life / Like a painful and beautiful day?"

My skin had turned cold and I tried to fight off the surging that was coming from my chest and going to my face, but the tears came anyway. I could not bear it. I got up and walked quickly from the room. I stood in the little cooking room for a couple of minutes and managed to collect myself. Before turning to the other room, I put on my glasses so that the priest could not see my stupid eyes. He looked up at me as I returned and sat back down. Just looked at me.

"Don't be afraid," he said, and took my hand. No gentler voice had ever reached my ears.

I asked him, now that I was back in my careful protection, if he had ever had any run-ins with the police.

He laughed and slapped the table. "Oh, indeed! Just the other day. I went to the police station to ask about a fellow priest who had been arrested at the demonstration and roughed up. Do you know what the police said? Oh my! 'You are not a priest, you are a lying bastard. Prove to us that you are a priest. You are not dressed like one and your rotten face does not look like that of a priest.' I showed them my identification and the fat man who was in charge said, 'You had these forged. Take them and throw them away.' Then he grabbed me by the shoulders and shouted, 'You are too nervous. You should get yourself a woman!' Then he turned me around and kicked me in the pants. 'Get out of here, you bastard troublemaker! And if we see you again we will smash your dirty face. You are a disgrace. A fake priest who makes such trouble!' " He laughed some more in genuine amusement. "That was really a farce." He shook his head. "Those poor chaps. Consumed with hatreds."

I gave him a cigarette and he sighed deeply. "I will go away soon, to England, to visit some priest friends." He stared out of the doorway toward the scrubby, wasted hills. "It will be nice to breathe a clean and free air. My lungs are beginning to choke in the atmosphere of this Spain. A human being needs to breathe well, and if he doesn't, he dies. Yes. A man can die if he breathes the wrong air."

A heavy-browed young man in a black sweater and thin old pants came in. His mouth was held in a wispy smile. He said hello and walked down the hallway.

"He is a gypsy boy who lives here," Father C. explained. "He came here to study to be a priest, but he fell in love with a social worker, a very lovely girl who has been helping a lot of his people who are living in this section, very, very poor and hopeless people. Now he works with her. They will get married and together they will do what they can to assist these lost families."

The sound of splashing water came from the back as the gypsy boy washed up. I asked Father C. to tell me more about the recent demonstration nearby when three priests were arrested along with about forty of the local people.

"It was disgusting and brutal the way the police charged the demonstrators with their horses," he said. "But even worse were the lies the government-controlled press printed. The newspapers said the whole thing had been perpetrated by a few working priests. That we had spoken and written lies about the government and made the people believe these lies, and then worked them into a passion against the government. As though we were evil maniacs. What awful lies! The terrible thing, you see, is that the people who read the papers, among them the middle class, of course, will believe these things and turn their backs on the priests and the workers. It makes one very sick."

We shared a long silence. I too stared toward the soiled, weary hillside out of the doorway and watched two little gypsy children in rags playing with a dog. Suddenly Father C. turned and, smiling wide, slapped me on the arm. "Don't feel bad. There is always some hope in this world. Come. I will show you this simple priest's house. It is decorated . . ." he laughed with total absurdity ". . . it is decorated with my childish hopes and prayers."

The two heavily tanned, serious-faced men were sitting on the steps of the church in Roncesvalles. The falling sun was glowing a deep red-orange behind them, and the little plaza vibrated in this passionate light.

"I will go to jail," one of the men said, spitting out a little tobacco from his cigarette. "I did not

*make any money for those two years. Why should
I have to give the government taxes for something
I never got?"*

*The other man yawned and said, "I can give
you an answer, but it would not tell you anything."*

A voice comes out of the voluptuous body.

"In front of the cameras I feel like a fish in crazy waters. Look for yourself: sudden strange noises, people who come and go, cameras that change position, persons who give instructions, other persons who contradict instructions, lights that go on and off. But I must tell you the truth. I like the chaotic situation of the studio. It makes me feel more vivid, more like myself."

A scrawny man with wild eyes trips over a cable and says "——" in French.

The voice goes on.

"I have made television and theater and movies. I like making movies the most. I realize, of course, that it sounds much more intellectual to say that I prefer doing theater. But I am not an intellectual, you see. I am a woman who wants to be an actress, a great actress. The truth is that to represent every night the same function, the same character, that is something boring. At least it bores me. I don't understand how anybody can do with love something that is boring."

The huge klieg lights are baking the reality from the studio, from the people. Small distances seem endless. Two men are pushing a large camera across the floor like sleepwalkers.

"To play is a challenge I enjoy and suffer very much. Trying to penetrate deep inside the skin of my character. It is like being my true self and at the same time yet living other lives. I am an actress of my generation because I am a woman of my generation. I could not be faithful to myself if I weren't faithful to my own time. That is all."

She lights a cigarette and begins leafing through a book. Her eyes are those of a gazelle that any moment might turn into a tiger.

"I'm Catalonian. From Barcelona. For quite some time now I have been reading everything important that is published in Catalan. Do I believe in God? Someone asked that of the novelist Jacinto Benavente, and he said sometimes yes, sometimes no." She smiles into the distance. "Yes, I think I believe in God. Why not?"

A beautician floats by and brushes the actress's eyebrows. A fat camera assistant a few yards (or miles?) away begins to giggle hysterically and his companion watches him in amazement.

The voice resumes. (Her jutting breasts breathe and move.)

"Becoming a good actress is a marvelous adventure. I do not know of anything so emotional. It is to look into others' psychological abysses. Interpretation doesn't only take intuition and talent, but a lot of practice, a lot of patience and vocation. Much, much discipline. Am I in love? Only with my work." Cool laughter comes out of the mouth.

Nervous people begin moving chairs and scenery. An absurd smell of electricity and perfume infiltrates the atmosphere.

"Sometimes I worry very much that I will get a psychological twitch from the characters I play. I like to be myself, nothing more. I don't like that fiction characters interfere with my own feelings or occupy my place inside or outside the studio. Here I am a character that I must play. Outside I must be myself. It is very complicated."

Smoke comes from the mouth. The voice is cool, and from far away it seems. "My hobby? I paint, but I do it very badly. I would be, I don't know, I would be kind of embarrassed to do very well something that I do only as a hobby. The thing is, you see, I must be perfect as an actress."

Over in a corner two men and a young actress are huddled together whispering. Another voice comes in now.

"Sonia! It is your turn. Hurry!"

An eyebrow arches. She drifts away.

"Ready?"

"Ready!"

"Scene one. Roll it!"

"Silence! Silence, please!"

The baking lights disembody sounds from bodies and things from other things. The whole business is called *Dark Dreams of August.*

The young director does not smoke but he bites his nails. He is very "natural," in a state of "anti-pose." His voice is grave. His studio-office is filled with books and photographs. There is no "taste" here.

"My new movie, *We Are Not Made of Stone,* is a synthesis, the history of man, typically Spanish. As in all of my pictures, in this one I follow my formula of humor, denunciation, realism, and poetry. Always much closer to a smile than laughter. But with a psychologic and social dimension behind the smile."

He used to be a painter who did not sell much but who appealed to an "in" group in Madrid.

"I like to create, and I like to see represented what I create. That is why I make movies."

He is married and has two children. He came from Sevilla.

"I like to discover new people, new faces, new situations. The movie has to be disintoxicated of so many sacred monsters. Of so many topical arguments. The windows must be opened for fresh air."

The star of his movie *The Game of the Oca* was a university boy who had never acted before.

"A real cinematographic industry does not exist in Spain. We are much closer to the art than to the industry. Our movies are personal movies, made strictly by vocation and personal adventure. We cannot compete with the big foreign cinematographic industries in techniques, but we can compete with them in imagination and originality."

He chews his nails and stares out of the window.

"The big techniques are many times just a costume to hide the lack of talent and creation. The movie is an art and as such should be cultivated by artists. I write the movies I direct . . ."

The phone rings. He quickly grabs it. "No, no. Call me in half an hour. Please."

His low, serious voice goes on.

"Yes, it is true I visit a psychiatrist frequently. Why? It is very simple. In Spain the people used to tell their problems to their neighbors and to their friends at the café and tavern. I'm not a man of cafés and bars nor do I like to chat with the neighbors. I much prefer to tell my things to the psychiatrist."

He has a cutting profile and is wearing a yellow sport shirt.

"I don't know who said it—youth is a state of mind. There are in this world too many people of thirty who are already old."

He carefully sips his anis.

"In Spain we still make an excessively clean and innocent movie. Most of the movies I see at international festivals would be considered much too daring for Spain. You know, all over the world, the same thing is happening—the search for a new voice, a new cinematographic language. Every generation has its own way of being and looks for its own identity, its own style of watching, feeling, of telling things. In Spain we are slowly crossing a bridge, acquiring a more real identity, our own. Godard? I like some of his movies, but they are too sophisticated."

His name is Manuel Summers. He has many non-movie activities. Judo, flamenco, skin diving. Right now he is studying hypnotism.

"Why is that little boy yelling so much?" the old man in the black beret asked. "There is no one in the street to hear him."

"That is why he is yelling," the sad-eyed woman replied, snapping the string beans that were to go into their midday stew.

The unsmiling baby-faced butler appeared without warning at my side and placed a fresh Scotch-and-soda on the gold and marble coffee table in front of me. I reached for a broiled shrimp and before I had touched my mouth with it he had taken the dish away to refill it.

"In my life I have had three gods," continued my aristocrat government-minister host seated on the sofa across the table. "Jesus of Nazareth, Albert Camus, and Marcel Proust. They have given me ideals and goals. The have given me my entire sensibility. Without them I would be a breathing empty shell." He lit an American filter cigarette and sipped from his thin Scotch highball. Looking down at him from the red silk wall to his right was a fifteenth-century wood statue of Christ on the cross. His face was thick with pain. "Without a moral aesthetic structure," my host went on, "man is nothing. Especially, and this is of the greatest importance, especially if he is in a position of responsibility to others. You see, one must truly belong to the people one serves. In fact"—he leaned forward and his long, sensitive face looked almost beatific —"in fact, one is this responsible belonging. Yes, absolutely. You could say that is existential—that one is what one does. A person is truly defined by his relation to others. Don't you agree?"

I said that I did. His elegantly lidded black eyes kept staring into mine almost as though they were pleading for some more confirmation than that. I looked away and at the grinning blackamoor that was holding the lamp. At its feet was a small photograph of a blond woman sitting on the veranda of a villa. She was in a bathing suit and she seemed amused. I asked López García to tell me just what those three gods had done for him.

"Christ gave me the concept and understanding of suffering for others," he said, leaning back and grinning happily. "Proust gave me a sense of style." He delicately tapped the ash off his cigarette into a silver shell ashtray. "And Camus—ah, I adore him so much!

His face, so like a sad, sad flower—that lovely tragic man gave me an understanding of modern man's dilemma." He munched a marinated oyster and carefully patted his lips with a black napkin. "We are all Sisyphus. Continually, eternally pushing that huge stone back up the hill for it to roll down again. Yes."

The impeccably unsmiling and relentlessly habited butler appeared at the side door with a plate of beef bits and mushrooms. López García pointed with his finger at the table, and the man put the plate down without its making a sound. I remarked on his efficiency. "Oh, yes!" agreed López García in his high, nasal voice. "He is quite lovely. I adore him. He has been with me a long, long time. He does not think with his head as we do. He thinks with the vibrations of his body. He is a true, true Spanish peasant."

With a quick, unannounced motion he put a record on the small phonograph half-hidden in an antique cabinet. A girl began singing bossa nova. He grinned at me, then suddenly leaped up. "Come! Let me show you my apartment. It is one of my great joys." I followed him. "It is my jewel box," he said, and giggled with pleasure and patted me on my shoulder. We were in a benign jungle of exquisite antiquities. Paintings, statue carvings, religious objects, plaster saints with tears on their cheeks, wrought-iron flowers. "Isn't that divine?" he said, pointing me toward a headless stone angel. "I am always asking myself, 'Where did she lose her head?'" He giggled again. "Very amusing. Perhaps a little irreverent, no? Ah, you are very understanding."

He led me into the bedroom. "I keep my modern painting in here. Don't ask me why." He made a capelike motion with his arm. "Picasso! Degas! Cocteau." I said it was all very impressive. Then I jokingly said that he must be very rich. He laughed and slapped me on the shoulder again. "No, no. Not rich. Come! Let me show you the view."

There through the softly breathing darkness lay Madrid, and the many lights in the city did not, somehow, disturb the darkness. López García suddenly turned to me. "Why did you come to Spain?" he asked, and his tone was not light. I told him, To see for myself what was going on in the country. The Spanish scene.

He looked into my face carefully and did not speak for a couple of moments, then he turned back to the darkly smiling city. "You know," he began, almost gently, as though he might be talking to himself, "we are contaminated by the political situation. All that outside people can think about is Franco and what seems to be our lack of political freedom. People seem incapable of thinking about the Spaniards themselves. I have been in many countries, among them your own, and the only country where one can be an individual is Spain. The only one. The patrimony of Spain is her people. They are unique. You must understand that human contact is of the utmost importance here. All else is really beside the point."

He turned my shoulder slightly to the left so that I could see the spire of a lonely cathedral in the sighing distance. "We are not a part of Europe," he continued. "We are Spanish. That should never be forgotten, otherwise the reality and the mystique of my country will escape you. This is a country of contradictions and extremes, wild extremes." A little laugh escaped him. "We defy your logic, which cries out for a simple answer, and that makes you angry. But that is too bad. Because of this thing that escapes you, we can have a private life. Artists, writers, architects, priests, peasants, all of them can live within themselves here and never be invaded by another person. Extraordinary, really extraordinary. Don't you agree?"

I said yes because I could not think of anything else to say. He solicitously guided me along the terrace as he talked. At the far end he drew me down to smell a box of red carnations. "People are always asking what will happen after Franco. My word! What difference does it make? Before, during, after—it is always Spain. The country of my blood, the country of my sleep, yes, of my sleep. You know, there is a sweetness here that you cannot find elsewhere. A monolithic purity." Suddenly there was the butler, with drinks for us. López García accepted his drink as he would the air. I found myself saying thank you to the man. "The Spaniard truly loves his country. With him it is not chauvinism"—he led me to a chic iron chair with a soft orange foam-rubber cushion—"it is not nationalism. It is simple dignity, unaffected. He is profoundly happy in this, no matter what other people, foreigners, try to tell him." Now he smiled in a special way at me. "Journalists are always writing the same stories about Spain. They have written these stories in their minds and hearts long before coming here. Why do they bother to make their visit? Why do they dislike the truth so much? Does it make them uncomfortable? Yes, I think it does. It disengages them from their silly fantasy. Ah! I have no interest in seeing them any more." And he made a gesture with his hand as though he were throwing them into the endless night. "The truth about my country—why doesn't someone write it? It would be so . . . so intelligent to do." He stared at the tiled terrace floor. "Ah! And then they ask why we are so suspicious of them! Does one throw one's arms about a slanderer? I ask you. It's really too absurd. This upsets me very much."

I asked him how long he had lived in this apartment with its marvelous view of the city. But it was a lost maneuver. "They think that to be gentle is to be passive," he said, looking at me with an expression of anger and anguish. "But they are wrong, so wrong. Such views are the result of an aggressive people, an angry culture." He looked at me with an abrupt softness. "I am sorry. I do not mean you," and he squeezed my hand. "Let us go inside," he went on, rising from his chair. "I will call someone very special. I want you to meet a real princess. She is so charming. You will love her too."

Back in his living room, his jewel box, he delightedly began dialing a number, and as he was doing this he said, "She is related to all the royal houses of Europe. Yes. She is not a small princess as some are whom I shall not mention." He spoke rapidly and intimately into the phone. "She is coming right over," he said, hanging up and plucking a black olive to his mouth. "She was in bed reading Dumas. Can you imagine! In bed with Alexandre Dumas! Of all people!" He twirled a large gold ring on his left hand. "One can have such a splendid time here in Spain. Such a splendid time. All you have to do is walk in the streets, sit in the cafés, to see how much the Spaniards enjoy each other's company. Where else can one find such preoccupation with humanity?"

As I was thinking about this, and with my eyes wandering around the madonnas and Christs and angels, the voice of Juliet Greco floated into the atmosphere from the half-hidden phonograph. López García was presenting me with his delighted expression again. "I must tell you about a wonderful, wonderful project I have for my children," he began.

I expressed some surprise, because I did not know that he was married. He giggled at his joke and my surprise. "My children . . . I mean . . . They are the children of the Spaniards who have gone to other countries, Germany, France, Sweden, everywhere, to work. Well, they do not go to school, you see. Those countries do not provide schools for their education, and they cannot go to the normal schools because, of course, they do not speak that language. So it is terrible for them. A child without a school is quite lost. It is his second home. You understand that? Quite lost. Well, I am going to these countries to arrange schools for them. Build them if I must. Because if they do not go to a Spanish school, how can they become complete Spaniards? You see? They cannot become themselves. And what is a Spanish child who is not a Spaniard? That is a terrible thought." And he made a gesture with his long hands of an infinite void.

For a few seconds we were both suspended in the possibilities of that terrible void. Juliet Greco had stopped singing and the only sounds were the traditionally mysterious ones coming from the pantry to our left. I reached for a mushroom and asked him if he spent the summers in Madrid. "My house!" he cried, exploding again into delight. "I have just built the most wonderful house in Ibiza. My own design. It is large and crazy and it is for my friends to enjoy themselves in." He clapped his hands and threw back his head. "Oh what a place! You must come there. This weekend. You will simply be wild about it. The sea there is so extraordinary. You will bathe there and forget everything that has ever troubled you. You will forget all the bad things you hear about Spain. It will take care of you like a good mother." He jumped up. "I will show you pictures of it," and he raced away through the exquisite red apartment.

While he was gone, I thought about what a friend of his had said a few days before. "López García is something, isn't he? One wonders how a man with his tastes and personality can make out so well in the mediocre atmosphere, the strange suspicious atmosphere of the government. Is he a fascist? Ah, one doesn't know. But he is very, very clever. He is an exotic but he is also very canny. He must know how to play that Franco game like an expert, because if he didn't, he wouldn't be there. You cannot be that important and be anti-Franco. He seems rich, but I suspect he lives way beyond his means. You cannot buy that stuff in his apartment with peanuts. He is quite an unusual one. He is very good friends with the American Embassy, and you must be an excellent game player to do that. Or else you must truly be one of them—a fascist."

> *The men were standing around the truck in the middle of the hot, bleached plaza of the village of Fuenterrabia. The truck was filled with tiles, and three of the village men were passing them to each other for inspection.*
>
> *"They are very expensive," a dusty-faced villager said to the heavy, hatless driver.*
>
> *The man shrugged impatiently. "Go to Zaragoza to buy them then."*

"One moment, please," another villager said. *"They are dirty."*

"Ah!" exclaimed the driver. *"You have rubbed the dirt from your hands on them. Listen, what kind of men are you? Bargaining over a bargain! How disgusting."*

The village men quietly looked at each other, then the youngest one said, "Yes. All right. I will buy fifty."

Manuel the Communist reminded me of an aging welterweight boxer who had put on weight but who could still go a few rounds without looking foolish. His rough, ruddy Cézanne face was scarred with smallpox pits. As he talked he would look around as if he were expecting someone to approach him. We were at the bullfight in Valencia.

Do you hate the bourgeois?

"No. I don't hate them. I feel sorry for them. They are so truly pathetic. They are sleepwalkers and don't know it. The world they have created and the world they are so terrified for is an infinite desert."

Do you feel the dynamics of class structure are really changing?

"Absolutely and irrevocably. All over the world the middle-class structure, that absurd castle, is crumbling. Nothing anybody can do can stop the historical march of Marxism. This is the logic of the heart, the natural way of life for the intelligent man. It is not something abstract that he reaches outside himself for and wears like a factory-made suit."

(The handsome young matador was holding his black hat and listening to his manager. He nodded his

*head as the other talked, but he kept his worried eyes
on the threatening gray sky.)*

What is wrong with the bourgeois?

"Everything it has invented is false and against the
natural growth of man. Its concepts of reality are insidious fantasies, and what they have created is a surrealistic world of absurd postures."

Is there any particular institution you could cite?

"Yes. The schools. What the middle class teaches
in its schools—which are, of course, the mandatory
schools of the human race—is the acquisition of data,
not the expansion of the mind and the heart."

*(The paunchy picador got on his heavily protected
horse with some heavy grunting and started exercising
it. When they came to the end of the courtyard the
horse just stood at the wall and would not turn
around. It seemed to have gone asleep. The picador
called it a dirty name.)*

What about the data of the teaching in the schools?

"It is so twisted and misrepresented that it is not
only useless but dangerous. It corrupts the minds of
the young and prepares them to be prejudiced and
vicious and unable to view life clearly and with an
open, agile mind. It is completely rotten."

*Do you feel this is true of the schools in the so-
called democracies? In the liberal middle-class schools
of America, for example?*

"Without any question. Show me, for example, one
book in America that tells you the true story of Spain
and her development and problems, her accomplish-
ments. Show me. Or in any other of the liberal democracies besides America. Show me a textbook that ex-
plains the complexities and purposes of the French
Revolution rather than some childish nonsense that

appeals to the feeble romanticism and prejudices of the author who put it together. That is where there should be a book-burning, not Germany. Burn as you would sterilize a gangrenous wound."

Do you feel that if the schools in the middle-class world were changed and good books substituted for the bad ones, that a true learning process could occur?

"Can one concentrate when covered with anxiety? Can one breathe when the air is poisoned? Can a bird fly in a vacuum?"

(Inside the stadium now the bands were playing their brassy traditional music, and the crowds were a mixed mass of giggles and candy-munching and peculiarly girlish impatience. A few feet from us a man with bad teeth was carefully sharpening the point of the sword.)

Tell me about the Church here. Does it have to be destroyed?

"Of course not. It has already destroyed itself. It is a barren ritual that has made passive slaves of millions and millions of good Spaniards, innocent Spaniards who never did anybody any harm. The paradoxical and very laughable thing now is that Marxism and the Church are working hand in hand. The Church sees that it is losing the workers and the only way not to continue to lose them is to work with the socialists and Communists who have the well-being of the workers at heart and also their complete belief. The workers deeply believe in the truth of socialism."

What about the future of this odd mating, or circumstantial wedding?

Perhaps this community, this dialogue—a word so loved and so misused by so many American middle-class fascists—will last, and perhaps it will fade and die. Depending on what happens within the Church itself. The more intelligent and contemporary thinking members of the clergy are with us. They know that the teachings of Christ have been distorted by the Church for its own protection and is power needs, its monopoly of the soul. Do you know the ironic thing is that the ecumenical agreements could have been written by Marx. Oh, indeed! Almost word for word."

(The crowd roared and within the umbrella of its sound a girl behind us screamed as the young matador slipped and barely missed being gored by the raging, bleeding bull.)

Can you see the ritual, if you want to call it that, of the Church and the people assuming a different shape, when things have changed, that is?

"In the future if the people want to go to church, they will do so consciously, voluntarily, as they might go to a play or a sports event or listen to music. For sheer sensual pleasure."

When I see most priests, I think of the women teachers of my childhood. They have something mysterious in common. Have you felt this?

"Very much so. Those poor chaps! If I had a simple-minded compassion I would say they mean well, but I don't think they do, unconsciously, of course. Like the teachers of your childhood—incidentally, those teachers never die, they live on in the shools of the world— they are castrates who have, in their choice of profession, rationalized their crippledness, their apartness from living reality, and told themselves they want to help the children, the young and the poor and the helpless. As if a eunuch could tell you how to get along with your wife! It is clearly the only work they can do —the only place where their incompleteness will be put up with. With their charges they can achieve a power they could not achieve in the normal world. So their position is simply one of power by default."

Tell me your feelings about Franco.

"Ah, that evil genius! Franco uses the lethargy of the masses as a good painter uses empty space on a canvas. He manipulates it. Under his crafty hand it becomes a living, breathing power. And, of course, he has managed to make himself a good friend of your government."

Will there be a revolution when he dies?

"We are in a state of revolution right now. It will get worse. I see blood, blood."

Have you thought very much about President Johnson?

"Yes, a great deal. He will destroy the world unless the American people stop him. He is like one of those dreadful giants of mythology. As his frustration increases, as he sees more and more that he is losing, he destroys more and more. I sometimes think he must truly represent the will or the unconscious of the American people. He was elected by them in free elections. So one can only assume . . ."

(*The terrified matador ran across the arena and leaped over the wood fence directly in front of us. In another second the bull smashed into it, and a piece of broken wood flipped into the air.*)

The popular explanation for the bullfight is that it is the Spaniards' way of triumphing over death. Do you believe this?

"That explanation gives the onlookers a certain charmed dignity. I'll tell you what I think is happening here. That bull does not represent death to them, as they like to tell you. It is themselves. They are taunting and stabbing and killing themselves. Just as a child who has been told that it is no good will finally become self-destructive and constantly hurt and kill itself, because it has come to believe the lies about itself. And at the same time it is killing the thing that made it feel this way because both have become the same thing in its mind. It is a ritual of self-murder. But you see, since it is a ritual the people are separated from the fact that they are not the spectators but the real participants. They think it is just a game they are watching. But they do not know it is a game in which they are the victims. You know, I think it would be a wonderful thing for the revolution if one could stop the bullfights. Just think of the fantastic, unbearable tensions that would overwhelm the people after a while. It would be like denying them sex. They would truly revolt and overthrow the lousy government. The thought of it makes me almost dizzy."

Is it true that strategists of the Communist Party are foreigners, French and Italian?

"Oh my God! How many times have I heard that lie! Of course, the socialists, Marxists, Communists of the world are brothers, but the Communist Party in Spain is directed by Spaniards. The fact that one learns and gets help from other people doesn't mean that we are under anyone else's control. If a man goes to hear Beethoven or reads Thomas Mann, does that mean those people tell him what to do, because they give him nourishment? It is against the Spaniard's nature to let outsiders tell him how to run his life. The government circulates that lie because they do not want the world to know that this is a true national movement, reflecting the hearts and beliefs of the Spanish people."

Are the Communists truly well organized?

"Oh, yes. And much better than the government thinks. It is not something vague and in words only. It is the only organized party in all of Spain."

How many members are there?

"I would say at least thirty thousand in Madrid alone. And ten times that all over the country."

Do they all pay dues, and do they all hold party membership cards?

"Most of them. And they meet regularly."

Isn't it dangerous for these people to be Communists? I mean, it is against the law, after all, to hold membership.

"Well, of course, we don't all flaunt our membership in the Party. But at the same time, it is not held a dark, dark secret. If an office worker is a member, the people around him know it, but not openly, if you know what I mean. There is a quiet acceptance of it."

(The bands were playing with wild joy and the spectators were yelling and shouting Olé! Olé! and waving white handkerchiefs to show their admiration for the fine kill. The matador was walking around the ring bowing and bowing and people were throwing candy and money and even the women were throwing scarves and gloves and pocketbooks into the ring for him.)

What about being caught and put into prison? Doesn't that frighten you?

"They would have to catch me first. And besides, I am not afraid. They have not made me into a coward. That is what they would like. They want cowardice to become the opium of the people."

Aren't the masses kept down by the memory of the Civil War?

"A new generation has come up. We are not frightened by the past. Listen, do you know what the corpse of the bull smells of? I will tell you. It smells of dead dreams, of cheap perfume, and stale cigar smoke."

The young men drinking in the café were buying lottery tickets. One of them, a big fellow with a blue sweatshirt, turned to one of the group and said, "Hey, George! Why aren't you buying one?"

"I don't want to," his friend replied. "The lottery is silly."

"But we're all doing it. You've got to do it. Hey, María. Make him buy one. You can't act like that. What kind of a bastard are you anyway?"

"U.S. REDS SPARKED SPAIN RIOT."

This headline in the international edition of an American newspaper shrieked at me like a psychotic Donald Duck. The report, filed from Madrid, said that a handful of American students at the University of Madrid had organized a flag-burning demonstration at the school. I had heard this accusation many times and had found it a routine government lie, but this was the first time I had seen such a charge in a non-Spanish paper. I said this to my newspaper friend, Walters, who was sitting with me in the Café Alemara in the Plaza Santana in Madrid.

He said, "Much of the foreign press, and by that I mean the English and American press, goes along with the government propaganda. This keeps them from really thinking about what is happening here, and also it's what their home offices want. It's part of the whole cliché structure. This kind of inflammatory reporting appeals to the reader and also manipulates him. Like calling a demonstration a riot, or saying something fizzled instead of ended. Outright lies and constant subtle distortion. Boy, what a wonderful profession to be in! Makes you feel real good."

"Is there any tieup here between the American press and the CIA?" I asked.

"Put it this way, the CIA and the American Embassy and the Franco government work hand in glove. So if a reporter is friendly with the last two, goes along with their interpretation of what is happening, he can't avoid being involved with the CIA. Our government has to back the Franco government up because of its obsession with Communism. Let me tell you a scary thing that happened recently. I bought three photographs which a freelancer had taken of a student demonstration. I mailed the negatives to my home office in London. A few days later an American correspondent who is friendly with the Embassy walked into my office with a print of one of the negatives. He had gotten it from the American Ambassador, who had autographed it because the correspondent's head was in the picture. He had been at the demonstration. Now obviously, what happened was my office in London had mailed the photographs directly to the Embassy so that the Embassy, and the CIA, could have pictures of any American students involved in any demonstrations. You know, 'American Communist agitators.' Nice, huh?"

"Very clean and lovely," I said.

"You know those three American girls who are being kicked out of the country for 'stirring up students' at a demonstration? Well, the newspapers said the Spanish government was deporting them. I found out that this isn't true. It's the American Embassy who is having them kicked out. Each of the girls told me this and I went to the Embassy and found out that the people there asked the government to act. Beautiful, don't you think? The girls had nothing to do with anything. They are no more agitators than you are. They were simply at the demonstration as were a lot of other people, and one of the girls spoke about treatment of the Negro in America. This makes them Communists. Oh, God!"

"What are the CIA guys like?" I asked.

"Oh, the usual all-American gung-ho types. Scotch-drinking, back-slapping, keep-America-strong Establishment boys. You know—jerks. And they don't try too hard to disguise their activities either. Not long ago a couple of them walked right into the office of a newspaper man who is a drinking buddy of theirs and said they had come for that list of American student agitators at the university. Real close family gesture, don't you think?"

He looked at his watch and said he had to run. "I've got to file a few lies," he said, and laughed slightly. I said I would see him the next day for lunch. The café was very comfortable and sympathetic. I decided to stay for a while. This was one of the bohemian cafés in Madrid, and also the one where the bullfight group hung out. At first glance, the two groups made an odd combination: the kids with their long hair, guitars, grab-bag clothes, and the serious, much older, and very Spanish bullfight types. But when you thought about it, you realized that they shared quite a lot. Both groups were objects of curiosity and awe, and both practiced a form of poetry. Neither was in the daily business of this world. That is a certainty.

The smell in this café was a warm and intimate melody of sausage, fried squid, wine, and musky tobacco. At the back of the café was a boy with bright golden hair down to his shoulders, and he was wearing a sweatshirt that said GANGES RIVER WHACK-ERS. A smiling girl with a butterfly tattoo pasted on her forehead was leaning on his shoulder and smiling her way into the endless present. At the crowded bar a lean, tense man with a lie for a face was complaining to his patient companion about a young bullfighter who owed him some money. Art is one thing, he was saying, but money is another. The limping, red-nosed old waiter who seemed preoccupied with complex distant memories shouted for two Fundadors. I had not been in a place like this since my old Village days. In those bars the other peripheral group was composed of hoods and hustlers in the rackets, and they thought all bohemians were faggots or defectives, but somehow we lived side by side outside the law. At the table next to me a girl in an army jacket was making small, tight drawings in a notebook. I looked closer and saw that the drawings were of the flora and fauna of her interior country.

As I gazed around at the faces—the late afternoon sun was spreading a delight of amber through the windows—I wondered what sort of fantasies the people here, including myself, were having about the others, and to what degree these fantasies, these immaculate projections, would later form realities that would go marching through the world as though they had an origin quite outside the viewer's mind; and whether these self-satisfied imaginings do not then beget others, and they too, and then finally the play is simply one second-generation-imagined reality examining another. And is that what is happening all the time? And are those frantic happenings that take place inside the head at night the true reality that got left behind, long, long ago?

I began to think about my two children and what I would put in my letter to them that night before going to bed. Could I tell them about my feelings and speculations as I sat there in that café? Could I recall for them my days in the Village and what I was like as a young man with both despair and love in my heart and literary demons roaring through my head like a fragment of a dream from the Dark Ages? Would they care? Would all that have any relevant meaning for them? I was a little saddened by the extreme difficulty, if not impossibility, of sharing with them that part of their father who was only seen by himself. Perhaps they would have to be content with their own fantasies about me. I could only hope that they would not be too far from the mark.

A couple of tables away the old waiter brought a glass of beer to a young man with a beard and black glasses. He asked for his money as soon as he put the beer down.

The Princess sipped at her Scotch-and-soda. "Is it true that they are going to do a Beckett play here?"

"Indeed," replied her companion, fingering his

polka-dot ascot. "Waiting for Godot. *Next week, I believe.*"

"*Beckett,*" the Princess mused, her lips wet with the Scotch. "*He is very strange, isn't he. Very . . . surrealistic.*"

Her companion chortled. "*In Spain his surrealism will seem like naturalism.*" And he laughed some more.

"I am a customer of hunger and defeat.
My clothes rustle with the music of despair.
My heels trod on pavements of nothingness. My eyes
    are mirrors."

The bony, sweatered young poet paced about the big room at the university. The transfixed students crowded the floor and leaned against the walls. The poet stared at the floor and paced. Suddenly he threw his arms into the air.

"The flowers in my garden sing themselves to sleep at
    night.
They feed themselves on their own blood.
And I, Carlos Oroza, am a mad weed in my own gar-
    den!"

The audience exploded into clapping and shouted, "Yes! Yes! Wonderful!" The faces of the painfully beautiful girls were ecstatic, and their shining eyes were seeing far, far beyond the room. The boys were very pleased, but they were still shy about showing the same emotion as the girls. They smiled knowingly and talked almost in whispers. The poet shouted:

"There is fear and trespassing is forbidden!
Here has ceased the ease of the pedestrian.
The reflection of a bayonet breaks the wing of a bird.
A fish commits suicide in the air."

He paused, holding his arms in the air like hot spears and staring furiously at the ceiling.

"Who among you can lick the foot of a cow?"

He dropped his arms and stood with a sudden overwhelming quiet. The kids clapped and shouted. "Marvelous, Carlos! Marvelous! You are divine! You have greatness!" and they turned to each other and poured out their pleasure and amazement.

Now the poet sat down in a canvas sling chair and stared into his hands as he rubbed them. He seemed utterly unaware that there were others around him. He began to speak softly.

"I tried to touch the Law's hand.
But I found a bruise of silence
Which her forehead had made up long ago.
I tried to kiss her lips.
But they were frozen.
And my skin tore as I pulled my mouth away."

A moan of agreement went out from the kids, and many whispers. A madonna-faced girl next to me whispered to her girl friend in a blue cashmere sweater, "I feel like crying." Now the poet lifted his face.

"My name is Carlos Oroza.
And I used to be in the country of the underworld.
On that ancient beach I grew in the hands of an old
*   sailor.*
The sounds I hear are the fish whispering my name.

*The octopus swims toward me with open tentacles of
    love.*
We are old friends.
*We grew up together in the silent seas of the mind's
    terror."*

Clapping and shouting and sounds of delight. The
wonderfully beautiful and alive girls were soaring.
"More!" a boy shouted from the rear of the room.
"Give us more, Carlos! We love you!"

Carlos looked up and a tender smile of completion
was on his dark and hawkish young face. He shook his
head. "I can't," he said. "There is no more in me today."

To my right a pale-skinned girl with long blond
hair was smiling and crying a little. She was holding
her books in her lap. Across from me a serious-looking
boy with curly black hair was staring out of the window, lost in a voyage of his own. Carlos got up and
started to leave. Several students crowded about him
and a rumpled boy with glasses put his arms around
him and kissed him on the cheek. We all began leaving the room.

"We were supposed to have the reading in an auditorium," Carlos told me in the babbling cool corridor.
"But at the last minute the school authorities said my
reading could not go on. So we all sneaked in here."

I asked him why the officials had done that.

He made a sound of disgust. "Ah! They are always
afraid if a large group of students assemble. And they
know that the students love my poetry so they think
they will get emotional and do something revolution-
ary, I suppose."

Two girls stopped near us, they were holding hands

and talking with their heads bowed. "Carlos' poetry excites me," one said softly, "but it scares me."

"Why?" the other asked.

"I don't know. It's almost like listening to something . . . something against the law. My parents would not like it at all. They would think it was, oh, dirty."

Carlos and I strolled through the faceless marble corridor, past the bored policemen at the gate, and out onto the street, where we stood for a few moments in a garden of smiles. A boy and a girl holding hands came up to him, and the girl said, "Carlos, you are beautiful. You help me to see new things."

"Thank you," he said smiling happily. "I like that."

"It was lousy that they didn't let you use the auditorium," the boy said. He was wearing a button that said Make Love Not War.

Carlos shrugged. "It is nothing. My poetry can get along without an auditorium." And he presented them with his sweet smile.

We strolled about so that he could say hello to several of the kids, all of whom were exuberantly responsive to him. He was like one of them, except that while their kids' faces showed warm dinners and attending hands, Carlos' showed the memory of small food and steep, cold stairways. I had seen several of the kids at an antiwar demonstration a couple of weeks before. Though the boys loved him too, clearly the girls were entranced by him. Not a one came close to him without touching him. From his station at the entrance, the sleepy guard watched the scene with a faint smile of routine contempt.

In a few minutes we were in a friend's car headed for Carlos' headquarters, or salon, the Café Gijon, the literary gathering spot in Madrid. As we were driving through the campus, where the new young willow trees were swaying slowly back and forth in the wind, the boy at the wheel said over his shoulder to me, "A beautiful prison." All the way downtown the kids in the car talked about a demonstration that was being planned for the following week. Carlos smiled and listened sympathetically and did not say more than a few words. I noticed for the first time that the girl next to him was holding one of his hands in both of hers.

The Café Gijon was shamelessly Carlos' living room. Whatever his real address, it was merely where he slept. A crowd was invariably awaiting the opening of his eyes. Several kids sat down with us at our table, and a couple of people who were not kids soon joined us. No one came up to our table without touching him.

"I am a kind of hero to them," Carlos told me, sipping a *café espresso* and ravenously smoking one of his endless local cigarettes. "Partly it is my poetry. The other part"—he shrugged happily—"perhaps I am a something inside them that the world says no to."

He laughed suddenly. "I am both Caliban and Prospero. . . . That's an amusing thought, just the same."

A balding, expensively dressed man in his forties came over to the table. "Carlos! All this attention is going to turn you into a bourgeois. I'd better watch out. Soon you'll be working my side of the street."

Carlos laughed and patted the man's hand. "He's an architect or something," he explained to me. A girl sat on each side of Carlos. One of them had red hair down to her shoulders. The old waiter with long gray sideburns leaned across the table and said, as he put the drinks of brandy and coffee down, "I should charge you more, Carlos. No one drinks when you are here. All they do is talk and look at you. You are bad for business."

The unusual businessman who had told me about the poet in the first place now began telling me more about him from his seat across the chattering jammed table. He had to almost shout because of the noise. But this did not make him conspicuous. "He is the most phenomenal thing in Spain," Pedro said. "Whenever he announces that he will give a reading, hundreds of kids are suddenly there. On a street corner, in the school. It's absolutely incredible. He has true charisma. And the most incredible thing about it is that all this does not bring him a penny. His poetry is free, like the air. He doesn't charge anything. None of his stuff is ever published. Of course, that's because he never writes it down. Nevertheless . . ."

Carlos turned to me and said, "My poems are born in my throat. And it is truly with a great sense of betrayal, even repugnance, that I write them down."

"He's a sort of troubadour," the businessman continued, holding a glass of brandy firmly in one hand and absently sipping it from time to time. "Like Villon and those people. He is a singer of the streets. He is really not of this century at all. Look at him. Doesn't he look like he could be a pal of Villon's in sixteenth-century Paris?" I looked at Carlos and nodded my agreement. Carlos laughed and slapped me on the shoulder. "All he owns is on his back," the other went on. "He's as poor as a mouse on a winter's night, but he could not care less. I have tried to explain money to him, but he simply cannot grasp its meaning. He doesn't want anything to do with it. I think he thinks it is a disease or something."

A girl came to the table with a newspaper clipping

and showed it to Carlos. It was a little story about the Russian poet Yevtushenko and Carlos meeting, and it said that Carlos had been snubbed by him.

"Oh!" exclaimed Carlos. "He didn't snub me. He had other things on his mind. Mostly himself."

The kids all laughed. Carlos turned to me and out of nowhere asked me, "Do you have any interest in the moon landings?"

I told him I didn't.

"I don't either. I feel the same way about finding the deepest part of the ocean."

The businessman continued his running biography of Carlos. "Do you know how he lives? I'll tell you. He sells books and magazines from door to door. How do you like that! A peddler. The finest poet in all of Spain is a door-to-door peddler. You can't tell me there isn't something the matter with that."

Carlos whispered something to one of the girls, and she put her head on his shoulder and laughed and laughed. He coolly blew a stream of white smoke into the air. His glinting black eyes were in a restless truce with this world.

"He lives as mysteriously as a priest on the run," the biographer was saying. "He says he has a room somewhere, but if you ask me it is more likely a corner in somebody else's room."

A fat girl with long earrings and a cupid mouth leaned across the railing from another table. "Carlos," she said, her voice high like something thrown by the wind, "I have written down one of your lines."

"Yes?"

"It is my favorite line," she said, and she quoted, " 'One must become crazy in order to ignore that we are all already committed.' It is brilliant, Carlos, completely brilliant."

"Thank you," and he blew her a little kiss. She disappeared behind the railing.

"I have a plan," the biographer went on, finishing his brandy and wiping his mouth quickly with a white handkerchief he kept in his lapel pocket. "I think I will arrange a reading concert for Carlos in one of the small theaters, and charge, say, a dollar admission. I think that's a very good idea. What do you say, Carlos?"

"That's fine," he replied, and waved to someone in the distance of the crowded café.

"What will you do with the money?"

"Oh, buy a very smart jacket, perhaps," and he laughed. "Or get drunk. Something absurd."

The businessman laughed and rubbed Carlos' curly black head. "You are a bad, bad boy. I am going to arrange it anyway." He looked at me. "If you ask me, Carlos is much better than those beat poets of yours. Ginsberg, Ferlinghetti, all those. More truly poetic. Not relying on the politics of the moment. Don't you agree?"

I said I did. Carlos looked at me and winked. The girl on his right had begun to read a book by Camus. Every now and then, when a particular pattern of conversation had completed itself, the expression of immediacy would leave Carlos' face and he would stare into the distance, as if for the moment he had fled that spot, away! away!, wheeling hawk-high in the unperjured blue. Then, when someone would call to him, or a hand would touch him, you could almost hear the whirring of wings as he swooped back. The telephone at the side of the room rang, and in a moment the old waiter called out, "Carlos! It is for you. It is another girl. My God! If I could only write a little poetry."

Carlos laughed and left the table, patting the cheek of one of his girl friends as he did. The businessman resumed talking: "Do you know what the wonderful thing about him is? He does not belong to anything or anybody. He is the freest spirit in Madrid." And abruptly his face was sad and he stared down into the empty brandy glass.

The American couple and their teen-age daughter came out of the cathedral in Toledo. A camera was slung over his shoulder, and his wife was carrying a guidebook. Their daughter walked ahead of them.

"They certainly don't make artists like that any more," the husband said.

"No, they certainly don't," she said.

"Simply gorgeous."

He casually put his arm around his wife's waist. Without breaking her stride, and without saying anything to him, she took his arm away.

"It's really a waste of time to go to the butcher's. Most of the meat is tasteless and what isn't is so high you can't afford it. And even if I did get a good cut of something, the cook would ruin it. She thinks that everything has to be thoroughly drowned in olive oil before it can be eaten. No matter how patiently I explain how the meat should be cooked, she goes right on doing it the same way. So I've given up."

I was having dinner with my friends the Parkers,

and Anne Parker was giving me a rundown on human survival in Madrid. She and her husband and child had been there for about a year. She was a freckled girl with abrupt movements, and she had lived in New York City for a while after getting out of Smith College. "It was the loneliest city I have ever been in," she told me. "Lonely and dangerous and completely fraudulent. Every moment I was there I longed for the reality and . . . and warmth, yes, warmth, of the New England town I had come from. There is no doubt in my mind that people lose their humanness in that awful city. It's mass insanity, particularly for a woman." From the back of their tile-floored apartment came the angry cries of a child. "Don't go in to her, Bill," Anne directed her husband, who was half out of his chair. "It'll just confirm her feelings that she can do anything with you. She simply has to learn the discipline of being alone. Let her cry it out. She isn't in pain or anything."

Bill looked at me, smiled in mild defeat, and sat back down. "Okay, honey. But if you ask me, I don't see why anybody should learn to be alone. It's that old puritanism in you coming out." And he laughed and took a drink of Scotch.

"Anyway," Anne went on, now that the question of child intrusion had been settled, "one of the first things we discovered after we got here was that there is no such thing as Spanish cuisine. It's a myth. Like the Spanish-Arab mystique. There are a few good fish dishes, which you really can't get here because Madrid is hardly a seaport, and the suckling pig is divine, no question of it, but that's it. The only place I've eaten a good paella is Valencia, everywhere else it's nonsense. The food here is simply survival food."

Bill looked at me and winked. Their child began to

wail at the back of the apartment again. Bill looked at his wife, a mock agonized expression on his face which said, For Christ's sake, honey, principles are principles but let's do something about the crying. His wife just smiled and shook her head to stave off any notions of going back that he might have. He sighed in traditional American father-doesn't-know-best resignation, and took another drink. "The best dish I've had here," he said, "is something literally called rotten pot. It's a kind of poetic stew."

"Where did it get that name?" I asked.

"Centuries ago, long before the Greyhound bus was invented, when people traveled in Spain they did it on foot or donkey, and they naturally took food along with them. Maybe the restaurants weren't any good even then. The most practical dish was a stew, of course. They would make a big batch of it, throwing in everything from goat meat to old love letters, and just heat it up when they were hungry. After a few days, of course, it smelled fantastic. So they called it rotten pot. Great, huh?"

Anne put a plate of almonds and a plate of olives in front of me. I asked them what they did for social life in Madrid. A dry, loud Ha! came from Anne. "Social life? You must be kidding. Bill's is his work and mine is the maid and the baby. I'm going stir crazy. We see a few Americans and English people, a few I said, but that gives me the feeling of a forced refugee gathering."

"I guess it is pretty tough," Bill said. "And Anne doesn't speak any Spanish, really. Why don't you study it, honey?"

"Ordinarily that would be a very sensible idea," she replied. "But I don't plan to stay here that long. I mean, I hope we don't stay here that long. I'd wind up speaking Spanish all right, but in a nut house."

Bill giggled. "Spaniards are strange in their social habits. No matter how closely you work with them, or how well you think you are getting to know them, you really don't. There is always a certain distance in them. They seem to protect themselves from any invasion of their privacy. Particularly from Americans. I guess you could call it aloof, but it's really deeper than that. It is like listening to flamenco music. You love it yet you know that you will never get inside it. Another thing. They never invite you to their homes. You see them out in public."

"That's funny," I said. "I felt they shared the whole place with me. Maybe most foreigners put them on the defensive," I suggested.

"Maybe," Bill said, thoughtfully.

Anne took an American cigarette from my pack and I gave her a light. "You know," she began, puffing hard to get the light from my cigarette, "they keep their women virtual prisoners. Both physically and psychologically. The men want them in the home while they go to the cafés and their friends."

"What do the women do?" I asked.

Bill giggled delightfully and got up to make himself a fresh Scotch. "They stay at home with the kids, watch television, and plot the murders of their husbands."

"I don't blame them," Anne said, and abandoned her chair to attend to the dinner table. "Keep your fingers crossed. Tonight's steak may taste like something you read about in the Grimm Brothers." And she headed furiously into the kitchen.

"Seriously," Bill continued—he was a sensitive, un-angry man with an easy, likable style, and I got the impression that he had been treated well as a child—"when it comes to personal relations, the Spaniards are still in the Middle Ages. Just as I think that, funda-mentally, they are terrified of progress because they might fail at it, so do I suspect that they are afraid to give their women any real, contemporary status, let's say in an Anglo-Saxon way, because if they gave them a break, or let them out of the dungeons, the women might keep right on going. This is the real reason for the protectiveness, I feel. Not so much a great valua-tion of the sacredness of sexual difference. The men are terrified and I think that basically they hate the women. Then, of course, the women get back at them in their own devious, midnight ways, so the score is even."

"Do the men have mistresses? In the French man-ner?"

"Well, not really. Maybe some of the upper class. But, generally, you know, the Spaniard is very sneaky about sex. You can't really tell what is going on."

"What about the new young woman, the one who is copying the English and American styles?"

He shook his head as he smiled skeptically. "They may look different from the old-style Spanish girl, but they're still puritanical as all hell. Those miniskirts hide a long black skirt that is made of iron, and God help you if you try to act like it isn't really there."

"And yet," I said, "one of the tourist lures is di-rected at the fantasy that Spanish women are demons of passion."

He chuckled. "Another of the cons. And man, there are so many."

We began eating at ten-thirty, a more or less normal time for Madrid, and I was starving. This was an advantage in eating the meat—it seemed to be a suppressed sort of steak—because as Anne had warned me, Spain was hardly one of the great gourmet countries. The salad, though, was splendid. It contained lots of sweet onion and odd-tasting tomato slices. We had strawberries for dessert.

"It's hard to believe," said Anne, "but the strawberries here are marvelous. Maybe they're really French." And she tittered and looked quickly at her husband, who just smiled and shook his head.

I asked her if she had gotten to know any Spanish women.

"I've met a few," she said, spooning away the last of her strawberries, "but I haven't really gotten to know any. They're very secretive and I get the feeling that they don't approve of American women. They think they're too forward or masculine or liberated or something. They are so accustomed to their own convent status that they are afraid of women who are not that way themselves. It's funny, but when I'm with them I feel peculiarly guilty. I want to apologize for being so free, and I want to reassure them that I am not betraying the cause of womanhood." And she laughed. "Maybe the American woman could use a little of this sense of conspiracy."

"I think they get back at the men in very subtle ways," Bill said, pouring some strong black coffee for me. "They may not have any real public status, but I bet they sure run the show back home. They let the men carry the ball out on the field, but they think up the signals. That's the way the game is run."

The baby began crying again. "No, Eugenia!" Anne

shouted, turning in the direction of the bedroom. "Stop being a bad girl and go back to sleep!"

The baby kept crying. Bill shrugged. "I guess the kid doesn't understand Castilian."

"She's really got to learn that crying will get her nowhere," Anne said, almost to herself.

A little later we went to a go-go place out in a new section near the airport. I had suggested another place, but Anne and Bill told me it had been taken over by the adults, so the kids had moved on to where we were going. "I can't believe it," Anne remarked as we drove through the dark Madrid streets that seemed to jump with all the darting honking little cars. "We're actually going out."

"Why, Anne, darling," Bill cracked. "You know you've never been happier in your life."

The go-go spot was packed. Most of the couples were young, but I saw about half a dozen couples composed of a young very pretty and busty girl and a much older, very well-dressed, and "cosmopolitan"-looking man. I had expected a band, but the dance music was coming from a record booth, where two tiny boppers were lounging with the young record operator. The music was insanely loud, and it was all American. The small dance floor in front of our table was roiling with couples who were doing their awkward best. Behind us, in a very large lounge, quite a few single young men were standing about in their sharp clothes waiting for some action to drop from heaven.

"Oh my!" Bill observed very loudly to get above the noise of the music. "They just don't have it. They just can't dance this stuff. It isn't in their blood or something. Look at that chick over there, the one with the big breasts and the matron's dress. She looks like she's running up an escalator!"

The dancers did indeed look out of touch with the music. The men were trying to get into the swing of things and yet at the same time to keep their dignity, and this conflict wasn't working out too well. The girls were going at it with less restraint; some of them were even assuming expressions of abandon and ecstasy that surely they had seen in movies, but the lessons they had learned in those convents were not to be beaten back so easily. I felt a mixture of pity and embarrassment: they were responding to two voices; the American Negro singer was exhorting them to go one way, and the droning of their childhood nuns another. I looked away and glanced around at the small jammed tables. Even the few girls who were smoking were not doing it right.

In a little while some of the dancers came off the floor, and others took their place. A sweating, tight-faced young man, who seemed also to have an aura of middle age about him, passed our table going back to his own. "I think I pulled a muscle in my back," he muttered to the girl whom he was guiding along.

"You must take things more slowly," she advised him. "The go-go can be very exciting."

A small group of young men who were clearly American soldiers, though they were not wearing uniforms, stood now at the entrance to the dance floor and looked the place over. They made me think immediately of all the crummy Westerns I had seen where the pistol man and his weak-faced sidekicks move in on an innocent bar and poison it up. They were grinning and slouching and obviously felt more at ease than anyone else there. They never stopped casing the tables and the twisting girls' bodies on the dance floor. I looked away, wondering when they would make their move.

"They're all over Spain," Bill said, noticing the soldiers. "It really makes you sick. These riff-raff American GIs wandering over Europe acting like they owned the place. . . ."

"But where are they supposed to go?" asked Anne.

"Why don't they stay home," he said. "I mean, way back home."

An imaginatively dressed and sexy couple now appeared on the dance floor, and in a couple of moments their expert frugging was stopping the other couples from pursuing their own exhausting ends. The kids were Americans, and their ease and skill was almost disturbing. Perhaps they were professionals, and this thought for some reason made me feel better. A hush had settled over the tables as everyone watched the couple.

The strong-armed, straggly-haired woman was busily arranging the oranges and peaches on her stand at the entrance to the rich-smelling market, while the shabby young man watched.

"You say such silly things to me," she said, turning a bruised peach away from its neighbor. "You should get yourself a girl friend."

"But I like you," he said, grinning.

"You should build yourself up, like my husband. He lifts weights."

"Why? To protect himself from you?"

"Oh you are a silly boy." And she gave him a coquettish little shove.

The government official patted his slightly perspiring face with a white monogrammed handkerchief and put it carefully back, folded, into his lapel pocket. His alert, slightly bloodshot eyes rolled from side to side, looking for something, I didn't know what.

"What continually amazes me," he began, "is the presumption of the Americans, both in an institutional way and personally, to judge so many other countries. It makes me think of the minister whose son is busy robbing and killing people while he preaches good behavior from his spotless pulpit. You know, I think that English Protestant snobbery is very much a part of the American character. Yes indeed. No matter how much your country thinks it has freed itself from its motherland, or -lands, because the other one is Germany, you still act and think in that crazy and often unbearable Anglo-Saxon way. Your patronizing of the Mediterranean peoples is a case in point. You think of them as dark, sensual, simple-minded, passionate beyond sanity, hedonists with no thought of the morrow, mad mystics, fascist brutes. They can do exactly the same things you do, say, in a political or religious sphere, yet you impute to us sinister motives, while you manage to claim that your motives are clean and disinterested. Dear God! You point to our art forms, bullfighting, flamenco, religious painting and sculpture, as demonic and strange things, reflecting a nature quite different from the Anglo-Saxon world, a nature that is unreasonable, interesting, yes, but explosive and unreasonable. Do you know what fascinates me? That the Anglo-Saxons have chosen these dark countries of the Mediterranean to vacation in and to spend their golden years when they retire from drudgery in their own countries. How contradictory! To come to the very places you have been condemning as dangerous. Do you know what? I think all of you are sick and you come to our sun-drenched, mystical countries to heal yourself. Exactly. That's what I think. Shocking idea, isn't it?

"But I will go further in this. Yes. Because I think a terrible but essential truth lies there that you have been avoiding. It is my suspicion that the Anglo-Saxons, with the centuries of puritanism and Reformation punishments behind them, with their fantastic cultural-psychological concentration on cleanness, light, correct, upright behavior and style, straight lines, manliness, and all that business, have had to cut themselves in two or force a part of themselves to go into hiding. A part of their psyche that their culture chastised and forbade. The dark side. Yes, the dark side! Do you see where I am pointing to? The dark side of themselves, which we all know to be the true side of oneself, eh? And they turned to the dark Mediterraneans and made of them their repressed dark selves, and they have been punishing this dark self for all kinds of imagined crimes which they themselves, of course, are guilty of, not us. But this part of themselves they truly love, as they should, and they come back to it whenever they can, come back to it on our shores. Am I right? Secretly they are ashamed of this dark self, they think it is feminine. And this is what makes them angry. They hate themselves for needing us, themselves, so they punish, punish, exorcise, really. Oh, it is really something, what goes on in your minds about us. A tragic Greek play, no less. Whenever one of your popular artists, or newspaper types, wants to depict a bad person, they paint him dark. Am I not right? Of course, you have to agree.

"If you could just let yourselves be more Spanish, your whole view of life would change. Your women would be happier too. They would be more natural. Unfortunately, your middle class brings up its females to think of femininity as weakness. Oh, what a terrible, terrible bit of nonsense.

"Permit me to tell you something shocking. The very thing you point to as our shame, our stain, as it were, is the thing we are most proud of. Our Moorish inheritance. Of course, in their confusion and desire to degrade us, the Angle-Saxons think of this as our Negro inheritance. The Moors were not Negroes, my friend. Their culture was the most sophisticated and advanced in the world. I am reminded of the little joke the Jews tell about themselves and gentiles: 'We were having nervous breakdowns when you people were still swinging in the trees.' Ha!

"Do you know what makes me laugh, sadly, of course. The myth that America is a true democracy and that everyone there regards everyone else as his brother and equal. I have lived in America, in Washington and New York, and I can absolutely assure you this is far from the truth. America is the most snobbish, discriminating country in the world. Just as it is one of the most aggressive countries in the world while telling everyone it is peace-loving. If you do not have certain social-symbol credentials, you cannot get in half the doors in Washington. If your daughter has not gone to one of the proper colleges, she is treated like an inferior by those who have, even though she is more intelligent. A person with an English background is always preferred over one with a Mediterranean background, socially and professionally. You can't deny that, can you?

"The Americans were terribly disliked when they first came over here. The army and the officials and experts. Their swagger and arrogance were simply unbearable. They thought that they were going to change us with their technology and power. Help civilize us. Oh dear! But the delicious thing is that we changed them!

"You ask me if I think the Spaniard has an inferiority complex. Well, let me tell you about that. He feels that he has been treated unfairly. He feels misunderstood. He is very sensitive to comment. But this is not unique with the Spaniard. You know, the wonderful thing about the Spaniard is that you can rally him to any universal cause. He will throw over everything else to fight for a cause. The more irrational and crazy it is, the more it appeals to him. He is anything but a materialist. You could almost say that he is a mystic in action. Yes, I like that.

"I have one great fear, and that is that progress of good living and possessions will change the Spaniard— perhaps. I hope we never become like the rich South Americans. They are so Miami. To be a Spaniard is to have an identity, and that is what we treasure the most —our identity. A Spaniard will give you everything he has, but not his identity. And that is what upsets foreigners the most."

The two little girls in clean blue smocks were walking lightly next to the towering stone walls of Avila.

"I should be at home now," one said, "but I

*don't want to leave you because you amuse me
very much."*

"That's nice," said the other, smiling at her.

*"I like Martha very much, but she doesn't
amuse me the way you do."*

*A bent old priest with rancid eyes pattered by.
He was whispering fiercely to himself.*

It was about seven o'clock and I decided to take a long walk before dinner. The walk would take my mind off my hunger. None of the restaurants would be open before eight o'clock, and I did not feel like going to one of the bars for *tapas*. They were very good—fried sardines, tuna fish, sausage, artichokes, even roasted larks—but they invariably satisfied my appetite without making me feel that I had really had dinner. I feel that I have cheated myself, and that is an absurd emotion. I was in Seville.

I left my hotel room and walked out into the plaza in front of the great cathedral. I stood there for a few minutes. I have always loved the plazas in front of European churches, particularly those in Spain and Italy. For some reason, I have always been alone in them, but this has never bothered me. The ambience there makes me happy, tranquil, and all together in a way that I have never felt in my own country. It does not seem so bad to be alone in Europe. I don't know why. The pale gray twilight sky was suddenly sprung into a terrible loveliness by a flock of wheeling black swallows. I followed them in their lyrical sweeping and darting and piercing-climbing and for those few moments I was back in the mountains of my childhood in Idaho, and I knew that something in this world made sense, if only you kept your eyes open to notice.

A package-tour group of Americans walked by me, headed for the cathedral. The four men had cameras, and the women all carried what I saw was tourist literature about the wonderful things to see and do in Spain.

"Wasn't that a fantastic lunch we had today?" one of the men said to the sport-shirted man near him. "All kinds of seafood snacks, roast chicken and that special rice they make, a couple of bottles of red wine"—and he nudged his woman in that sly, "aren't we naughty" way—"salad and cake and ice cream. And it only cost about three bucks. Three bucks! Where could you get all that in Baltimore?"

"Do you think the Arabs lived here too?" a woman asked.

"Oh sure. They got around a lot," someone said.

I had been thinking of going inside the cathedral for a while, but now I decided not to. The presence of other Americans in such places usually made me quite uncomfortable. But then, tourists of all kinds affect me the same way. I always wonder what it is they're really looking for. I stared up at the massively serene spires, thinking, what was in the daydream minds of the men who put them together stone by stone? came down the spires, yard by yard, watched a boy turn and say something suggestive to a girl with tanned legs and gay breasts, then pulled myself away from that scene of filtered innocence, and moved on.

I avoided the main streets, because after business hours they gave me the creepy sensation of walking into an apartment after the party had ended, and walked, instead, in the intimate, amused little side streets, where the cars and the pedestrians weaved in and out of each other. In this ballet of passage you almost never heard the honk of a car. The drivers of the tiny cars knew that you knew they were coming, a delicate play of vibrations was at work, and just as the car fender approached a body it moved easily and carefully away. There were never any sounds of anger, as there would have been in the streets of my own country, and even when people, in moving on and off the sidewalks and streets in that ancient closeness, happened to collide, it was a soft collision and eased by smiles. I loved the smallness and the humanness of these streets.

Somewhere a guitar was playing. It was exquisitely part of the sounds and smells of the street, not something alien and abstracted and alone in its action, and I followed it, spinning lightly away from a car here, side-stepping a sudden human presence there. The man with my name who had waited with premature exhaustion in the departure section of the airport in New York was still there. I was someone else. The fretting guitar sounds led me to a workingman's bar. The song of the guitar in the back room seemed, at a stunned moment, to be the sound of the men there, and in that uncanny moment, I felt farther away from everything I had been than ever before in my adult life.

I sat in the back, near the old guitar player, and an angular-faced woman with black diamonds for eyes took my order. Now the man began to sing in that high, tense keening way of the flamenco. A group of tanned, muscular workingmen drinking near me clapped their hands—a striking of stones, it seemed—and urged him on with cries of Olé! Olé! and statements like "Oh yes, marvelous," and "Truly it is so." His song was about a boy and a girl in a small village who were slowly driving each other crazy with their love. I could hear those stone clappings traveling for centuries. I had the waitress take a glass of brandy to the old man. Over in the corner a girl in a tight red sweater began to snap her fingers in and out of the music and smile to her boy friend.

I very much needed food. I looked at a handwritten menu—how do they learn to write that way?—and the waitress told me that the kidneys in sherry served with rice was a very good dish. So I had that and a salad. When the old man finished we all applauded him, and when he walked around with his beret held out every-one gave him a little change. He was very polite in his response, and no one there felt blackjacked about giving. It was a pleasure.

The kidneys were indeed excellent. They were not beaten down by overcooking. The cook knew that kidneys without that unique snap to their texture were a chore to eat. Two men behind me were having a conversation about making a living in this town.

"We just don't have any choice," one man was saying. "It's either that way or nothing."

"Yes," the other agreed, "when you're in business here you get screwed."

"I might as well drop it all and spend my time in the cafés and enjoy the company."

"At least you would not be destroying yourself."

"Exactly. It would make some sense."

Over in the corner the girl who had been snapping her fingers was holding hands with her boy friend, a man with big rough hands, and keeping her smooth handsome face close to his as she talked. A somnolent madonna on the wall was also watching them. A man at the bar in front began to laugh loud and happily, and I turned to see him give his companion—both of them were dressed in dark blue overalls—a big strong hug. "You are a very crazy fellow, Luis," he said, "but you are all right."

I went to a main street to have *espresso*. It was crowded with strollers and groups of men having arguments without rancor. They used their hands with eloquence and grace. The big maple trees overhead rustled unobtrusively, and the clean air was a joy to breathe. I bought a copy of *Time* and sat in a sidewalk café. The cigarette and the strong coffee were a small but direct and authentic pleasure. Then I began reading what *Time* had to say about the Basque people, and outrage stomped my good feeling. What despicable words! "Comic opera feats." "Basque troublemakers." "Their own archaic language, an agglutinated monstrosity." "And they all wear the black berets, that are the main contribution of their culture to the western world."

It sounded like obscene government propaganda. And for what? I asked myself. For what? Gratuitous and vicious and untrue. No wonder wherever I went in Spain the first barrier I had to jump was a distrust of Americans. I felt quite ashamed, and because of this I overtipped the waiter. I got up and walked away, leaving behind the magazine. I quickly rejoined the crowds so that I could recover the good feelings that had been contaminated.

Walking again—it was more of a flowing, a drifting in and out of, because in New York I *walked* to work, *walked* to go to the bank—I found myself concentrating on the faces of the people more, staring at particular Spanish details of stores and buildings, gestures of differentness, in order to kill the dirty-taste feeling left in me by reading the insults in the magazine; and, with a microscopic urgency, I was seeing a full, curved mouth, a thick brooding eyebrow, a stone flower on a façade, and as I was thus healing myself, I began to analyze why I felt so tranquil and no longer in small angry pieces when I was in places like the church plaza, or a narrow cobbled street in this and other Mediterranean countries. Was it due to a bit of auto-suggestion which makes the grass elsewhere always greener? Or was it because of something more valid, something that the con men of tourist bureaus did not have in mind when they wrote those illiterate induce-ments to fly away? I could isolate one feeling for sure —that I felt more like myself, in those places, than I generally did in my own country. And feeling more like myself meant, quite simply, not feeling those other personalities that I had been forced to invent to deal with those countless situations and humans in New York that I, the me of myself, did not want any part of. The stage of me became so crowded with those others: a ghostly repertory company that refused to go home when the curtain came down. Those other hungry, manipulated, angry pseudo-humans were not with me here, and it was me and me alone that was responding to and becoming part of—no longer a spectator, object scene—the fold in the stone martyr's robe, the reflection of light on the shy wet street, the ache in the tolling of the bells. The singleness of my-self allowed me to discover how much a part of this natural world I truly was.

I passed a woman and child waiting for a bus. The woman gave the child's hand a restraining pat. "Don't eat all the candy now. Save some for the bus trip."

"But I want it now," the child said, its voice high and flute-clear.

"You'll want it more then."

A one-legged man brushed by me as I crossed the street, and before I could excuse myself he had asked me to excuse him for being awkward. In front of me two pretty girls were walking slowly, arm in arm and giggling. Farther on, a young man with half-closed eyes was leaning in a doorway and humming to himself. I turned into a crooked old street, a great-grandmother of a street, and headed back to my hotel. A round old priest holding a black brief case hummed softly as he looked into the window of a men's clothing store. Church bells clanged hugely in the night distance, and within their clanging suddenly appeared three American sailors at the end of the street. They paused uncertainly under a corner light and looked up and down the deserted quiet street. I turned left at the next side street and went to my hotel that way.

> *The black-veiled old lady sitting with her family in the Granada pastry shop was crying. "I feel his presence every minute of the day."*
>
> *Her heavy, middle-aged daughter took her hand and stroked it. "But Mama, you must stop thinking of the dead."*
>
> *The old lady pulled her hand away. "Nobody can tell me to stop thinking of my husband! He was my life."*
>
> *And she bent her head and cried and cried.*

"I used to think I could find myself and my destiny somewhere else," the Madrid businessman was saying as he puffed angrily on his American filter cigarette. "I lived in France and England. I worked and went to school and I said to myself, 'Juan, there is nothing for you in Spain. It is dead. It is too crazy and dangerous a place for you to live. You must find yourself here in these other places. You have a future here.' Well, I lived for years abroad. As far as I was concerned, Spain was a memory that I could do without. But do you know something? I was not myself. I was lonely and quite unhappy. I was a victim of my own delusions and my own inability to know where I truly belonged. I was destroying myself by trying to become someone else. I was beginning to believe all that stuff about the Black Legend. Oh, do not misunderstand me. I am not saying this country is perfect, or that the government situation has always been the very best. But what government is perfect?

"There were great struggles to go through. Franco maneuvered us through them. You have no idea how skillful he is at those things. Well, I returned to Spain and discovered that I should never have left. This is where I came from, this is where I belong. If everybody left as I did, what sort of a place would this be? And then, there is the dignity involved. How can one hold one's head high after abandoning his own country, which needs him? Tell me that if you can. And please tell me how a man can live without dignity. Oh, I know that many people do, but can one say that is living? Eh? Living in shame is to be half dead, believe me.

"Well, I returned here, and slowly things began taking a shape. I discovered that one can really do whatever one wants here. You are rewarded for your effort. The business possibilities are unlimited. Each year our concern does better and better. We are doing business with firms all over the world now. The government does not interfere with us at all. I am not interested in politics, and that is the way it should be. Those people who are are playing a very dangerous game with themselves. Why don't they just settle down to living their own lives? What is all this foolish noise? These demonstrations? Who are they doing any good? Please explain that to me if you can.

"I am back here among my friends and I am quite happy. Yes. Quite happy. I have a lovely new apartment and I have a wonderful girl. And I travel a good bit. What more should I ask of this world? Should I throw all of this away for some crazy political ideology? I have come a long way to return to my country. I do not intend to wreck myself with such foolishness. Things are very good now."

The two middle-aged women dressed completely in black were standing in the old stone doorway chatting. One was breaking little pieces off a fresh roll and chewing them slowly. They stopped their talking as two quite beautiful and developed young ladies in brightly colored, very high miniskirts came walking up the street. The women stared at them.

"Good heavens," one of the black-dressed women said. "Just look at that."

"Yes. I am." She made a tsk-tsk sound with her tongue. "Pretty soon they will be hiding nothing."

"Then the men won't have anything to dream about. It is a shame."

The man who was a member of the Civil Guard (he was dressed in street clothes now) sat in his brother-in-law's house in Tarragona and sipped at his glass of white wine. He was in his forties. A fastidiously trimmed mustache kept you from completely seeing a very thin, tight upper lip.

How long have you been in the Civil Guard?

"Almost ten years."

Why did you join it?

"Why not?"

Is the pay any good?

"Not any good. It is about eleven dollars in American money. But I live in the barracks and we get our food free there."

Is it very different living there than in a regular house?

"The others there are good fellows. It is not a lonely place."

Does it bother you being a policeman?

"No. It is like anything else. I don't think it should bother me."

What are the most important things to you?

"Important things . . . you mean besides food and sleeping and . . . let me see . . . a person's mother, his country, and his job. The Church too, of course."

Do you think people are afraid of you?

"They know that a policeman is the law and you do not do anything against the law. That is very bad."

Have you ever been at a demonstration or a protest?

"Oh yes."

What do you think of the people who are in them?

"They are crazy to do that. They only make the government angry, and they do not change anything by the way they act."

Are the Communists behind them?

"There is no doubt about that. Those dirty people give nice people bad ideas and when the trouble starts, they run away. They should be put in jail, every dirty, bastard one of them, and kept there."

Do you think the demonstrators have a good reason for doing what they do?

"Mostly they are stupid reasons. Oh, perhaps the workers have some cause, but then they should go to their syndicates if they are not happy with the situation they have. That is what the government made the syndicates for. Those fellows should have more respect for their jobs. They are lucky they are not starving."

Have you personally had to arrest any protestors?

"Oh, I have had to take care of a few. To show them who was boss and that they were doing things against the government. Some nasty ones, you know. You have to hit them sometimes. They make you angry with what they call you. I have had stones thrown at me. No man likes that kind of thing."

What about the women?

"It makes you sick when the women say things to you. You want to smash them in the face for being like that. It is unnatural for a woman to be in a crowd of crazy people like that. They don't know what they are doing. They should feel ashamed."

Where do you come from?

"The south, near Málaga. A little town called ——. Most of my people are still there. They have little farms."

Did you like it there in ——?

"The life is hard and there is not much a fellow can do if he does not work on a little farm. It is quiet, very quiet. I liked it when I had to go into the army. The discipline is good for you. It makes you strong. The Civil Guard is like that. It makes you feel strong and you are doing what your country tells you. You are not just loafing around in your life. Many fellows, that is all they do. And they get foolish ideas, and they become no good."

Did you ever think of becoming a priest?

"My mother wanted me to do that. But you had to study a lot. I had a cousin who was a novice for a year in Granada, but he never got enough to eat. He was always hungry, so he left and became a fisherman. But I think you eat more as a priest now."

Do you admire Franco?

"Of course I do. You know, we must not discuss these things. I should not be talking to you at all. You know that. But because my sister works in your friend's house, and your friend asked that I see you. As a favor. But we must not go into things about the Generalissimo."

What do you do when you are not on duty?

"Oh, have a drink with one of the fellows in a café. I like the bullfights very much. Sometimes I see one of the women. But that is for just a little while. You must see a woman from time to time. It makes you feel better. You understand."

What will you do when you retire?

"I don't know. Maybe go back to my town and work at the farm. Maybe live here with my sister. Maybe I won't do anything because the world could be blown up and all over with then. So I say to myself, leave the future alone.

On the television set in the corner of the room a soldier was jumping his horse over a hurdle in a show at Seville. The sound had been turned off and this made the man and his horse appear to be in another world, a world of motion without any sound. It made me feel absurd and afraid.

The camera switched to the crowd. The people were shouting and clapping soundlessly. Before I knew what I was doing, I touched my left hand with my right hand. I had to confirm at least my own existence.

The American family finally located a table that pleased them in the Segovia restaurant. While the mother and father were arranging three of the four children at the table, the fourth, a boy of about ten, went to the wall of the room to look at the display of paper money from many countries.

"Ours looks the best," he said, coming back to the table. "That other money doesn't look right."

Secrecy and passion—such was the music of my meeting with the Basque underground representatives. On a lonely green mountain outside San Sebastián, a simple virginal mountaintop that had heretofore known only the whisperings of trees and the madrigals of birds, that was where we met, the pale elegant one, the muscular dark one, and I. They both kept looking about as we talked, just to be sure that we were safe from whoever might be dangerous.

"The Franco government has done everything it can to destroy us," the dark man was saying, "beating and torturing our factory workers, putting them in jail by the scores, deporting hundreds to the south and forbidding them ever to return, forbidding the teaching of Basque culture to our children in school, even at one time outlawing the speaking of our language in public places."

We strolled along the narrow black mountain road. To my left, miles of valley loveliness away, was the bold blue of the Bay of Biscay. "Everything the government has done with us has been a betrayal," the vibrant dark man went on, "legally and psychologically, spiritually. Our government has been driven into exile, we have been denied a voice in Madrid, we cannot meet to discuss our destiny without fear of being arrested and molested by the Civil Guard or those filthy secret service people."

The thin man spoke quickly in Basque to him, the words rich and sensual, like the marvelous *tapas*, that tempt you in the bars. He was apparently warning him to lower his voice because a tiny white car suddenly appeared around the bend, but it scurried on. Even I was apprehensive about the police, my muscles tightening at every alien sound.

"The Franco hatred of us still persists from the Civil War," he continued, the thin man contributing from time to time in that unforgettably expressive tongue. "The Basque army was the first to form against his bunch and so many died to keep Franco from stealing Spain. We are still being punished." He was momentarily changed by a thought of despair. "I wonder if anyone cares but us."

I told him most people, unfortunately, thought of the Basque people, not in terms of their courageous fight for existence, but patronizingly in terms of their "folk culture."

Both men laughed harshly. "How absurd!" said the thin man. "But you know, this folk culture serves us well. We use these things, like folk dances and music entertainments, as disguises for meeting with large numbers of sympathizers. We turn them into freedom meetings. They beautifully serve the underground."

"All of the Basques are together in this so-called underground," the muscular man told me. "We are all struggling for the same thing, our liberty, our identity. Many, many contribute money to the cause."

Now a rain began to fall, a soft, feminine rain, but a wet rain, and we decided to drive back to San Sebastián, to a Basque workingman's tavern. "It is so important that we speak to you, a free member of the world press," the thin man said, as we curled back down the anxious mountain. "The government-controlled press in Spain either tells outright lies or does not mention events at all. It creates spaces of nonexistence."

In the crowded, noisy, and happy bar the Basque men were drinking and eating and laughing and playing their tricky game of cards called *chin-chon*. They clearly loved each other's company. A tall piercing-eyed man drinking wine at the bar began to sing in Basque, unaffectedly and without stopping the activity of anyone around him. In a minute several other men joined him in this lovely, lovely song. I asked my friends what it was about. "It is an old, old song," the thin man explained, chewing on a small hot sausage. "It is about a man who lives as a hunter and how he loves the woods and the animals. He has just been married, and he is wondering if his wife will understand his love for these things or will she become jealous and force him to give them up."

I spent a long time with them in the bar, hearing about the Basque movement, the efforts of its members, both in Spain and in exile in France and America, to keep up the fight. "We will keep fighting until we are recognized or until we die," said the dark man quite simply.

Later on, after the rain had spent its sweetening self, we went to an apartment, and I listened to a tape recording of the May Day demonstration in San Sebastián, when thousands and thousands of Basques braved the police and the Civil Guard in the hot streets.

The noise of the crowd was almost overpowering. "Liberty! Liberty!" a man shouted, and the crowd roared and pushed at the police cordon.

"Down with fascism!" a woman yelled. "Down with Franco!"

Then they began throwing stones at the armed police, in their jeeps, on horses, and on foot. The clunk of the stones hitting the steel helmets was as real as anything I had heard in my life.

"Come on, you cowardly bastards!" a man shouted. "Shoot me. Go on. Shoot me if you have any courage." The crowd roared and the police shouted orders to them that they ignored. Then the crowd sounds swelled into the Basque national anthem, and goose pimples of emotion rose on my skin. Someone yelled an obscenity at the government.

At the evening's end, we went back into the street, and parted there.

"It was gracious of you to come to us," the dark man said, and the other nodded. I told them I was grateful to them for seeing me. We shook hands, and they walked rapidly down the slender glistening street. Suddenly the thin man turned and shouted, "Please! Do not forget us!"

I waved back. "I won't," I said. I couldn't. To do

that would be to forget myself. They vanished into the darkness.

> *The man lying on the floor of the police van held his handkerchief to his bleeding, smashed mouth and listened to the Civil Guard and the wild demonstration outside.*
>
> *"Kill them!" pleaded one of the guards. "Let's kill one of them. That will stop them. Please, captain!"*
>
> *"Stop it, Jorge!" the captain commanded him. "Control yourself."*
>
> *"Show them! Shoot them!"*
>
> *Then the captain slapped his face to calm him down.*